The Horizontal Epistles
of Andromeda Veal

Adrian Plass
Sacred Diarist

PRESENTS

The Horizontal Epistles
of
Andromeda Veal

Fount
An Imprint of HarperCollins*Publishers*

Fount Paperbacks is an Imprint of
HarperCollins*Religious*
Part of HarperCollins*Publishers*
77–85 Fulham Palace Road,
Hammersmith, London W6 8JB

First published in Great Britain in 1988
by Marshall Pickering and re-issued
in 1991 by Fount Paperbacks
7 9 11 12 10 8

A catalogue record for this book is
available from the British Library

ISBN 0 551 01617 5

Set in Plantin

Printed in Great Britain by
HarperCollinsManufacturing Glasgow

Contents

PART III

PART IV

PART V

Dear Reader,

A real miracle has happened. Anne and Gerald think I've had a good idea! When I first told them I was going to collect Andromeda's correspondence from the time she was in hospital, they both tutted and clicked their tongues and made sighing noises. Anne said, 'Oh, really darling . . .', and Gerald ended up grinning that infuriating grin of his. They thought I was going to get carried away by another of what they call my 'loopy obsessions'. I reminded them that lots of people have been interested enough to read my diary. Anne was gracious enough to nod and say, 'Well, that's true enough, dear', but Gerald sniggered and said that considering the fact that it was supposed to be a serious book, an awful lot of people had got a lot of laughs out of it. I pointed out that Edwin, our elder, had wept over a number of the entries, but that just set Gerald off cackling to himself, so I didn't say any more at the time.

I'd better explain about Andromeda's letters.

We first met Andromeda (aged seven at the time) when Mrs Veal had to go into hospital, and Edwin, who is Andromeda's uncle, asked if we could put his niece up for a few days. She turned out to be an unusual little girl with a *very* strong personality. We took her to church with us on the Sunday and she caused a sensation to put it mildly! It's all down in my diary (which, despite Gerald's comments, *is* intended to be a sort of spiritual log for the use of future generations, and *not* a religious joke book). Anyway, as I was saying, Andromeda caused quite an impact in church, and also in our family. She adored Anne, she was fascinated by Gerald, and she referred to me as 'The fascist'. She had lots to say about the rights of women, most of it learned from her mother who's a christian feminist, and she had no qualms about saying it – especially to me! After she'd gone,

9

Anne said she thought there was a lot of worry and tension underneath Andromeda's very grown up way of talking, but I couldn't really see it at the time.

Then, a few months later, Anne got a letter out of the blue from Andromeda, saying that she was on traction in hospital after breaking a femur, and that her parents were not around to visit her. The poor little scrap sounded so lost that Anne decided to mobilise the whole church to help. It was amazing! So many people wrote or visited over the next few weeks. Frank Braddock, our neighbour, wrote a story specially for her, Gerald sent her several letters, Charles Cook sent her two or three rather strange communications from Deep Joy Bible School, and even old Leonard Thynn put pen to paper a couple of times, although the results are – well, read them for yourself! Mrs Flushpool dropped her a line (full of advice and warning of course), and Vernon Rawlings sent her one of his duplicated 'non-begging' letters every now and again. Loads of others wrote, including me – I sent recent extracts from my diary for the times when Andromeda fancied something a little more serious. I'm afraid I couldn't stop Anne's Uncle Ralph from writing. I think his letter is just a bit – well – 'Ralphish'. Still, he meant well. Meanwhile, Andromeda wrote lots of letters herself, some to people in the church, and some to famous people or world leaders, like Cliff Richard and Margaret Thatcher. She never actually sent the 'famous people' ones, but she obviously meant every word!

It was when I was round at Andromeda's house, sometime after she left hospital, that her mum and dad showed me the letters she wrote and never sent, and the ones that people sent to her. I liked them so much that I decided (with Mr and Mrs Veal and Andromeda's permission) to go round all the people in the church and ask for copies of the ones she *did* send. I probably haven't collected them all, but people were very helpful (especially Father John out at the monastery). I think I've got most of them.

When I'd got them all together and in order I showed

Anne and Gerald. That's when the miracle happened.

'A good idea!' they said. How about that?

Oh, one more thing – when Andromeda stayed with us, the only thing that would really keep her quiet was Gerald's personal stereo. She got a bit confused though, and always referred to it as his 'Personal problem'. I'm glad I remembered to tell you that. You might have been a little puzzled by Andromeda's constant references to my son's personal problem!

So there we are. I hope you enjoy reading these letters as much as I enjoyed collecting them.

Yours Truly

Adrian Plass.

PART I

Dear Anne,

　　　I hope you don't mined me writing to you, but I am in trubble. I am an attraction in hospital. Muther has gone to be with the green and common wimmen and I am all aloan. I have fracchered my lemur trying to eat mewsli and rollerskate at the same time. The state have got me horizontall.

　　PLEESE WRITE. I am surrounded by impressed wimmen, and plittically unconscious children. Tell the fashist he can write too if he wants only no thacherite claptrap and remember I'm a mizz.

　　Tell Geruld I ~~wouldn't~~ woodn't mined having his persunnel problem to play with while I'm horizontall.

　　Anne, who are the green and common wimmen? Muther says they are stopping Prezident Raygun from putting american bottoms in our fields. She has gone with her

15

frend Gwenda, the one father used
to say makes Cyril Smith look
anorecksic. Muther was going to
stay when they made me an attraction, but Gwenda said love only
means you buy a logical bond and
the green and common wommen
needed her more.   Gwenda said
lonliness must be fighted. I have
fighted it Anne. I think I have lost.
Please write to me. I even have to
pee horizontall. They left me something
to read, but there aren't many pichur-
es in the Soshulist Worker.

Do you know where father lives now
Anne? I know he is a laccy of the
capitallist pigs but the logical bond
he bort for me must have come from
a very good shop. He mite come and
see me if he heers I'm an attraction.

I have asked God to come and help
me, but he hasn't turned up so far.
        PLEESE WRITE!!
           Logical bonds,

           Andromeda Veal (Mizz)

P. S. If you find out where father lives, coold you give him a note for me pleese Anne. It's in the ennveLlope with this letta.
Thancyou.

Dear daddy,
      Please come and see
me or wright to me or fone
me or sumthing, eh?
     PLEESE daddy

    Logical bonds

     Andromeda

Darling Andromeda,

I've just read your lovely letter. Thanks so much for writing to me. We've *never* forgotten your stay with us. I did three things as soon as I'd read your letter. First, I made a gingerbread man for you and put it in the oven to bake, then I wrapped Gerald's personal stereo up to send with some tapes, and last of all I sat down to write back to you.

You have been in the wars, haven't you? I'd love you to write back and tell me more about the accident and what the doctors said and did. Would you mind doing that?

I think it's American *bases* that Gwenda and mother are protesting about, darling, not *bottoms*. It must have been a very difficult decision for mummy to make, but I'm sure she misses you terribly and will be back soon. I'm afraid I have no idea where your father lives at the moment, but I'm going to ask your Uncle Edwin who, as you know, is the Elder in our church. I've given him your note for daddy as well. I expect he'll come and see you, and so will I soon. You must be *so* uncomfortable, you poor love. The other thing I've done is to write down a list of lots of names and addresses of people in our church, and I've sent you plenty of paper and envelopes and stamps so that you can write to them. I'll get Uncle Edwin to tell everybody you're going to write and I'm sure you'll get loads and loads of replies. I've told Uncle Adrian (whom you quite rightly describe as 'the fascist') to send you some extracts from his diary from time to time, and Gerald promises to write too.

Be brave, sweetheart! Remember Jesus loves all little children, and he's already turned up without you knowing it. See you soon.

Love, Anne.

    X X X

Dear Anne,

I cryed a bit when your parsel came. Mother's frend Gwenda says tears are a sign of weekness, but its hard to be strong when you are horizontall, Anne. You mustn't call them gingerbread men by the way. Muther made me a gingerbread <u>person</u> wonce. She said the men sort are sexist. Yours tastes just the same though. I hope there are no harmfull addititives in it. Gwenda says that bad temper and murder and rape and war are all caused by harmful addititives. She and muther said they were going to only live on grapes once because all the other food was full of harmful addititives. Gwenda said that in a few days they would be tall and strong and clean. By the third day they were crauling round the kitchen floor pewking up bits of grape. I stuck to having mewsli every day. It is a bit like eating your way out of a haystak, but at least you don't pewk up. Father used to annoy Gwenda when he was still living at home by saying he wanted a nice fat E102 sandwich for tea. I don't think father liked Gwenda. I hope Uncle Edwin finds father soon, Anne. My logical bond hurts.

It was orful when I broke my lemur, Anne! Muther said I had fifteen seconds to get my rollerskates off, eat my mewsli and get reddy for bed. I tried to do them all at once and fell down. When we got to the hospital a man looked at my leg and said he was the sturgeon who was going to mend me. He said he was called <u>Mister</u> Fisher. Just my luck to get an uncwollified one! He said I'd got to be an attraction for weeks and weeks, so here I am. Oh, Anne, it's a real pain in the base!

Thanks for the persunnel problem and all the stuff. Are you sure Jesus has turned up?

Logical bonds

Andromeda.

P.S. Do you think you've got just a
bit of a logical bond for me, Anne?
Do you think you mite have?

Dear Andromeda,

Anne Plass has just phoned me to say you've had a bit of a disaster! You really do things in a big way, don't you my adorable little niece. I wish Mum had let me know before she went, but never mind — we'll cope. Anne says she's sending you lots of stationery, and I'm going to let everyone in the church know that letters would be appreciated. No point being an Elder if you can't use it sometimes, eh, cherub? I'll be along to see you of course, and I'm sure there'll be a few others coming to stare at the only Veal in captivity! By the way, why not drop a few lines to some of our world leaders? You never know, you might change the history of the world!

As far as getting in touch with your dad is concerned, I'll do my very best, but, as you know, he did leave home rather suddenly, and so far no one I've asked seems to know where he's got to. Don't worry though — he's bound to get in touch eventually. He's always been quite crackers about you, Andromeda, you know that. We'll all be praying for you, love. See you soon.

Best wishes,

Uncle Edwin.

P.S. Don't give the nurses too hard a time, honey. They're
not used to political activists like you!

The Gremlin,
 Red Square,
  Moscow,
   Russia.

    Dear Mister Gorgeouschops,
       You don't know me, but I am a
small english soshulist called Mizz
Veal — Mizz Andromeda Veal. I am
eight and I am an attraction in
hospital. Pleese don't think you've
got to stop   your breckfast in the
 Gremlin kitchen just to read my
letter. I know you are very bizzy
and ockupied in Affganistan and
trying to get the pollit-bureau open
and stopping. Prezidant Raygun from
watching Star Wars on the moon,
but I wanted to ask you sumthing.
Everyone says you are not like Linen
and Starling and the bald thick one
who fighted with tables at the Untied
Nations. The thing is — I was wun-
dering if I could be your speshul
adviser when I am bigger. I can't
do much at the moment because
the state have got me horizontall

til the bones nit, but I am a sosh-ulist like you and I could help. I know ruffly where Margaret Thacher lives, so I could show your G.B.H. agents which tube to get off at if they wanted to infiltraight her when the reverlooshun comes. Also I could warn you when birds fly over-head so you don't get those nasty splodges all over your head! Your Russian pigeons must be a size Mister Gorgeouschops!

One thing I don't like is your camps. They don't sound much fun. Mother read to me about one in a book called A day in the life of Ivan Something that sounds like a sneeze, but I think Starling was Akela at that one so I'll let you off.

By the way my frend Geruld (we share his persunnel problem) told me that Neil Kinnock is an anagram of I knock Lenin. Puts you off a bit, eh?

Logical bonds,
Andromeda Veal (Mizz)

P.S. Don't tell muther I wrote will

you? She says Russian soshulism is a load of crab, but I think you look nice.

P. P. S. We've got one of yours over here already. He's in charge of lots of minors and he's got two brillo pads stuck to his head. His name is sumothing like Half a lagers brill.

P. P. P. S. Have you ever had to pee horizontall while you've been in charge of Russia?

Dear Andromeda,

Name of Thynn. Leonard Thynn. Friend of the Plasses – well, think I'm a friend. *Am* a friend. Sure of it! Friend of the Plasses. Adrian: tall, friendly, simple type. Anne: sweet, lovely, wonderful. Gerald: good lad, speaks his mind, not everyone likes what's *in* his mind. I do. Took me home and helped me to bed once when I got a bit – tired. Yes, definitely a friend of the Plasses. They certainly like *me* – well, they seem to. Quite often borrow their cat for – never mind what for. Used to have some pets myself. Cat called Brandy. Budgie called Soda. Two goldfish called Ice and Lemon. Funny eh? No, not really. Bit of a give-away actually. Got a little problem – well, not a *little* problem, more of a *big* problem, with thingy. Drink. Too much, that is. Yes.

Anyway – 'nough about the wretched Thynn. About you, young Veal! Hear you came a cropper. Bust your whatnot. In for running repairs, eh, girl? Well – not *running* repairs. Silly word to use really. More like 'hanging about' repairs. Femur I'm told. Fearfully fiddly fings femurs. Bit of a joke there. Well, not quite a joke, more of a – well, bit silly really. Always rather enjoyed alliteration. That's when all the first letters are – sorry! Drivelling on rather. Habit of mine.

Look! Thought I'd tell you a funny story. Cheer you up a bit. Not very good at it, but I'll have a go. Starts after the next full stop. This chap – walking through a forest. (Doesn't have to be a forest, you understand. Could be a wood, copse, clump – any sort of arboreal assembly, as long as trees are in the picture. Got it? Good.) Well, this chap is walking (or he could be strolling or ambling. Not striding. Striding spoils the story), he's walking, strolling or ambling through this forest, copse, wood or clump, when all of a

27

sudden he notices a little chap (not abnormally little, I don't mean, more sort of at the bottom end of the 'not a dwarf' range), and this comparatively little chap is squatting behind a tree. I expect you're saying to yourself, 'How did the chap (the one walking through the forest, copse, etc. . . .) notice the little chap at all (the squatter, that is) if he was behind a tree?' Well, the answer is that the squatter, vertically deficient though he might have been, was significantly broader (in the squatting posture at any rate) than the tree behind which he squatted. Clear? Good.

So, then the strolling chap calls out to the squatting chap (and we're getting a lot closer to the funny bit now), he calls out, 'Hello!'. Then the squatting chap − presumably craning his neck round his tree to see the strolling chap − (actually, he's probably not strolling any more − probably stopped just before addressing the squatting chap, but I'll go on calling him the strolling chap so as not to confuse you. Okay?) − now where was I? Oh, yes, the squatting chap calls over to the strolling chap and says, 'Hello!' back. Then, the strolling chap, who obviously doesn't have even a passing acquaintanceship with the smallish squatter, says, 'What are you?', and the chap replies, 'I'm a tinker.' Then the stroller says (and this really is the final bend before hitting the old punchline − *ever* so funny! Well, *I* think it's funny − well, *quite* funny), he says, 'What are you doing squatting behind that tree?' And the chap answers (I'll put it on a separate line because this is IT, the joke proper), he says:

'I'm tinking.'

Get it? I'm *tinking*. What are you doing? I'm *tinking*. Good 'un, eh? Hope it's not a bit too − you know, bit too thingy.

Anyway, sorry about the leg and − the leg. Told mother I wanted to write to Andromeda. Poor old Mum. Deaf as a post. Said if I wanted to bite a chronometer I must be even loonier than she'd thought. Still − sent her love when she understood. Said a prayer with her about you last night. God's alright. Doesn't give up, not with me anyway. Do slip sometimes. Doesn't give up. I could tell you some stories – anyway.

Regards,

Thynn (Leonard).

P.S. Do hope the funny story was, well – you know.

Greetings in the name of one who is strong and mighty in deed and word to usward – able to give and provide from his marvellous bounty more than the simple heart of man can imagine, to bring salvation and eternal life through the outpouring of his boundless love to we who, in the latter years, were lost in sin and death, and through his great and immeasurable love to bring us at last safely to heaven's shore through the storm-tossed waves of that sea of life, the crossing of which is the portion of all men until we are called in the fullness of time, and on a day that was appointed and fixed before time began, to be with him for all eternity in the distant and shining place where all is peace and contentment because he is there and prepares a dwelling for us that we might also, undeserving though we be, inherit a kingdom of everlasting joy – from one saved and brought to repentance by that same grace from the sinful and rebelliously hard-hearted nature which all men since Adam have most shamefully endured, and brought finally after tribulation and the ministry of the saints to the knowledge of joy in-working through his soul, by the matchless and powerful movement of that heavenly will in one who shall throughout all ages be deeply thankful for that wonderful beneficence, and awaits with humble obedience the call that will herald his translation into Paradise – to a sister and partaker in the mystical body wherein we all share, who, caught up in the blessed mystery of saving power is one with the saints and martyrs now and through the life hereafter –

Dear Andromeda,

No time to write more now. Will write again soon.

Love, Charles.

Dear Andromeda,

Uncle Ralph here – Anne's uncle really, but I could be yours as well if you like. Anne said you were in for a stretch (Gettit! Stretch! Traction!), so I said I'd write and cheer you up with a few of me jokes. Rib-ticklin' Ralph they call me at work (among other things! Know what I mean?). I went to hospital once with a pain in the neck, but she left after I'd settled in. Eh? Anne said leave the jokes out, but you need a laugh, don't you? Pretty little nurse looked after me when I was in. She said, 'I'm just going to give you a little injection Mr Surtees, I hope it won't put you off me.' I said, 'You couldn't give me the needle if you tried, Nurse!' Laugh! I nearly asked for a bottle. They were a good bunch those nurses, though. Loads of patience. Mind you, they'd have nothing to do if they hadn't got any patients, would they? (Gottit? Patience – patients. Eh?). Doctors were a bit of a miserable lot. I said to one, 'Look, doc, I've had three different bits of me taken out in the last five years. You sure you haven't got a deal on with the local take-away?' Didn't even smile. He must have been foreign. The ward sister was a bit of a gloom and doom merchant too. Tried me best to cheer her up. I'd smuggled this bottle of imitation blood in, see? So one day after I'd asked for the bed pan and they'd put the old curtains round, I tipped it all down me chin and me chest, and hung over the side of the bed with me tongue lolling out and me eyes all wide and staring. Did she bite! I'll say she did! Panic! Emergency! Did she swing into action, or did she swing into action! Then, when she lifted me back on the bed, I grinned at her and said, 'I've finished with the bed pan, Sister.' I've never seen anyone so angry. She got her revenge though. Won't tell you how – let's just say that with friends like her, who needs enemas? Eh? I think the Italians call 'em innuendoes. With me?

I'm coming your way soon, so I'll drop in and say hello. Don't do anything I wouldn't do!

Cheers

Uncle Ralph.

P.S. What's the difference between a nurse with something in her eye, and a boil that's getting better? Answer – one's a blinking sister, and the other's a sinking blister. Gettit? Good 'un, eh?

Dear Anne,

Thankyou verry mutch for arsking yor Uncle Ralf to rite me a letta. It wos a bit of a funnee letta tho Anne. He said he was going to put lots of jokes in to chear me up, but I coodun't find a singul one! Still, he sounds nice and happee.

Anne, I think I mite write to Geruld if that's orlright. Muther said he sounded like one of the plitical corpsis yew see warking about aul the thyme but he was very frendly when I staid with you eeven tho he took the micky owt of me and said that FEMINIST is a nammagranam of I FIST MEN, and wen I said I diddun't thinc that wos verry funny he ticcled me and maid me larf, and woodun't stop untill I said — Corrunashun Street is maid in Personchester — three thymes. There hasn't bean mutch larfing in our house lately, Anne. Muther's frend Gwenda said

33

that wen the reverlooshun cums,
jokes will be judged on hou fare
they are to mineority groops, and
farther said – are yew seeriously
saying that joaks doon't have to bee
funnee ? – and Gwenda said – that's
rite – and farther said – in that
cayse Bob Munkhowse must be the
Chay Gavara of commedy – and
muther put his pipe terbacco in the
food mixa with sum jelly.

Oh, Anne, I carn't tell yew what
it's lyke to be stretched owt withowt
a pairent. I wood eeven tork to a
raiving fashist antee – reverlooshun-
ery if they wood be kined to me lyke
a pairent, but doon't tell ennyone
I said that, or Kneel Kinnerk
will nevver let me cum to his partee. Who do yew vote four, Anne?
I think yew shood be the leada of
the NICE partee, I do. Cum and
sea me soon, eh?

Logical Bonds

Andromeda.

P.S. Geruld's not ingaged or enny of that, is he?

34

Dear Andromeda,

I was so sorry to hear about your fractured lemur – I mean femur. Gerald asked me to say that he hopes that you don't end up with one leg shorter than the other. He said if you do, *he* can't do anything about it, but he knows a man who can. I think he's going to write to you soon. Now that *will* be a miracle!

Anyway – Auntie Anne says she thinks you might want to read an extract from my diary. I can't think why. It is, after all, a serious document. I hope it's not too 'fashist' for you . . .

Thursday

Read a great article in a magazine called 'Jam for 21st Century Christian Families Who Don't Buzz Any More'. All about enjoying God's natural creation. Decided a good old family ramble was called for. Anne agreed. Gerald, in one of his cynical moods, said he was fed up with 'rambles, quiche, light jokes, cherryade, harmless fun, and all the other pseudo-Christian baggage that gets dragged around the church'. Got cross with him and insisted he comes on Saturday.

Prayed hard tonight for good weather at the weekend.

Friday

Distinctly overheard Gerald praying for rain as I passed his bedroom this morning. Locked myself in the bathroom and prayed for sunshine again.

We shall see!!

Rang Richard Cook and invited him along too. Gerald said he'd only come if he could bring a new girlfriend called

Noreen, who's not a Christian. Agreed rather doubtfully. Hope she gets on alright with Richard. He is such a *Christian* Christian.

Saturday

Woke to brilliant sunshine. Tried not to look smug over my cornflakes. Gerald very glum.

Set off, all in our car, at 10.30 am. Absolute cloudburst the instant I switched the engine on. Ignored Gerald clapping in the back and carried on anyway.

Poor old Richard Cook was jammed in the back between Noreen, Gerald's girlfriend, who turns out to be a very large girl, and Noreen's pet, Paws, who is a huge black hairy dog.

After a while Richard said, in a muffled voice, 'Is your mansion booked in Paradise, Noreen?'

Noreen stopped putting on her bright pink lipstick for a moment, and said, 'No, love, we're just 'avin' days out this year. Can't afford to go away.'

Richard told her he'd meant was she a Christian, and

added that he was a charismatic. 'You know what that means do you, Noreen?' he asked.

Noreen said she did because she'd had an uncle who had to stick this thing up his nose whenever his tubes got blocked.

''Ere!' she went on, 'You're not one o' them mormons are you?'

'Certainly not!' said Richard through a mouthful of Paws. 'I abhor sects!'

'Not much fun for your wife then,' said Noreen dispassionately.

Blank silence.

Richard said, 'What a charming dog, Noreen.'

'Y-e-e-e-s,' said Noreen affectionately. 'Say hello to Uncle Dickie-doos, Pawsy-poos.'

'Oh dear,' said Gerald a moment later, 'Pawsy-poos has sicky-pood all over Uncle Dickie-doo's shoesy-woos.'

Stopped and let Richard out to clean his shoes with handfuls of grass. Sun came out immediately. Put Richard back next to the window beside Gerald. Stopped a mile later when Gerald was sick all over Richard's shoulder because of the smell.

Nobody hungry when we got to the picnic site. Everything smelled of dog vomit. Paws stole a ham and a huge trifle from the picnic basket while no one was watching. Richard went white and asked if there was a bus back to town.

Went for a short walk but had to dash back when the rain started. Richard begged pathetically to be allowed to sit in front. Anne sat next to wet Paws, who wasn't sick once on the journey back.

Arrived home and all got out of the car. Fine rain and sunshine at the same time.

'Ooh, look!' said Noreen pointing upwards.

We all looked. It was a beautiful rainbow.

Gerald and I smiled at each other.

Anne nodded wisely.

Paws brought up the trifle.

Richard said, 'I know I am not renowned for verbal flippancy, but were you aware that "God's creation" is an anagram of "Dog's reaction"?'

See you soon,

Love, Uncle Adrian.

P.S. I do hope we end up friends despite our political differences.

Dear Geruld,

I eggspect your muther has told you I am a horizontall attraction at the moment what with the lemur nitting and everything. I play with your persunnel problem all the time so I don't hear much, except when your Uncle Ralf vizited me and he pinched Nurse Roundway's base and she screemed so loud I heard it right through the beejees. I like Nurse Roundway. She smiles like a apple. I thort she'd report Uncle Ralf to the sturgeon, but after he'd gone she arsked if he was coming again. Tell you what though, Geruld — she's got a loony family. Last night she arsked me if I wanted sumthing to read so I told her I'd got a Soshulist Worker and muther doesn't let me read chilldren's books becouse they poison the mined, speshully Eden Blighted, the one who farther told me writes the Newrotic Nine books.

Gwenda said that Goldiloks and the three bears should really be called Arkytipal woman despretty struggles to snatch a few crumms back from three vicious myth-images of male dommination.

Anway, Nurse Roundway said (yor not going to beleeve this Geruld) she said that her little neece who is the same age as me, won't go to sleep unless she's bin able to cuddle up with her <u>poo</u>. I know it takes all <u>soughts</u>, Geruld, but that strikes me as dissgussting, and I thort we were talking about books anyway.

The fashist you live with sent me a bit of his dairy. I liked it. I liked Paws. I've never had a pet, Geruld. Father was going to get a dog wonce, but muther woodn't let him because she arsked him what he rearly thought of Gwenda, and he said "Clothes by Billy Smart and perfume by paranoya." I've never had a dolly either, Geruld. Muther says they are sosieties tool for reeinforsing the subjektiv female roll, but Gwenda said I could have a little plastic man I saw in a toyshop as long as I cauled it Bigot. I luvved Bigot, Geruld, but he got broke when muther threw him at father after she said that Gwenda fild a big space in her life and father said it must be a blinking grate gap if Gwenda fild it.

Pleese come and see me Geruld and tell the fashist I woodn't mined a bit more dairy. Pleese pray that muther will come back from the green and common wimmen soon.

All my logical bonds,
Andromeda

P.S. Did you notiss the bit where I said I havn't got a dolly, Geruld? They are bad things but it woodn't be my fawlt if sumone gived me one wood it?

P.P.S. Eh?

Cosmos Evangelism Outreach
Universal Conversion College Project
Prefab Number 3
Armistice Row
Bagshot

Telephone (Bill awaits faith income)

Dear Brother or Sister,

Please excuse the faint print and poor quality paper of our newsletter but funds are low as we enter the ninety-eighth phase of our project to build the Universal Conversion College. As you know from our previous letter we are aiming for a total sum of 23.5 million pounds. At present we have just topped the thirteen pounds fifty pence mark and it is marvellous to see the work grow. Only last week one of us found five pence in the precinct, and we have also had a number of Tizer bottles donated which should realise a return substantially close to the sum of thirty pence. It is a great encouragement when you are living by faith as we are, to see how all that is needful is provided. We eat regularly (it is my turn to eat on Tuesdays and Thursdays) and it is amazing how many games and activities can be successfully organised in the dark. It occurred to me last night, as I lay trying to sleep on the linoleum, that our policy of never asking for financial support is what separates us out from those projects which seem to be constantly begging. The space provided at the bottom of this letter for Barclaycard numbers is purely intended for those who feel personally led to share their wealth and comfort with brothers and sisters fighting a lonely battle on the rugged frontiers of Christian endeavour.

Some have queried the fact that one of our original prophetic words to the effect that the college would be built and the whole of England and Wales converted by last Wednesday, has fallen a little short of fulfilment. We now feel led to say, however, that we believe this to be due to a spirit of meanness in some individual outside the project. We prayed for him or her last night as we read the story of Ananias and Sapphira by candlelight. Do you know that story, friend?

Yours,

Vernon Rawlings (sic sec)

P.S. We are also anxious that you should not leave large sums of money to the college in your will, unless you are absolutely sure that you wish to support the Lord's work, rather than leave the money to people who are already comfortably off.

P.P.S. We are studying the book of James at present. What a fine message it presents!

PART II

Dear Anne,

Muther rung me up this mourning from a place near the green and common wimmen. It was a very bad line. I arsked her if Mister Raygun had bin for his base yet, but she said there are still a lots of crude rissoles behind a fence, so she can't come back yet. She said she cryed last night when she thought of me being an attraction and horizontall, but Gwenda said it was just a bad cayse of G. M. T., and G. M. T. always makes wimmen tense. I arsked Nurse Roundway what G. M. T. means. She said it means Grennich Mean Time. Why does Grennich Mean Time always make wimmen tense, Anne? Are we all going looney or what?

A man in a backwoods collar came round today Anne. I was the only one he spoke to. He said he was ~~cauled~~ cauled the Neverend Boom, and it was his first time in the hospital. Just before he went I arsked him why he hadn't spoken to ennyone else. He said it was because I was the only one with P for Prottistant at the end of my bed. He said all the others had R.C. for Roaming Catlicks, C.F. for Christian Felloaship, or B. for Baptists or S.A. for Salvation Army. He'd gonn before I cood tell him. P. is for Porridge and R.C. is for Rice Crispies, and C.F. is for Corn Flakes, and B. is for Bran, and S.A. is for Stewed Apple. I thort I was the stupiddist person in the world, Anne, but Neverend Boom wins by a mile.

Did Geruld notiss the bit in my letter where I said I havn't got a dolly, Anne? Becduse I havn't got one of those bad things. If he gets me one I won't upset him by not taking it. I will pretend I like it.

Logical bonds
Andromeda

P.S. If Jesus only likes good little

girls, I don't think he will like me,
Anne. I am affrayed I was pleased
when muther said she cryed.
Yes I was, Anne.

Darling Andromeda,

Just a quick note to say that there's one address I didn't give you that I meant to. Do you remember, sweetheart, when you stayed with us, you met Father John? He was dressed in a long brown cloak and he was going rather bald on top. Now I come to think about it, you didn't actually *meet* him, but you saw him in the next door garden talking to Frank Braddock, our neighbour. Father John is a very kind, wise man, and I know he'd be only too happy to help with any problems you might have. Do write to him if you want to, darling. The address is on the back of this letter. See you soon.

Love Anne

X X X

Hey, Andy Pandy! Gerald here!

What's going on? I hear you lost a battle with a stone floor and now you're on the rack down at St Whatsit's. Thanks for your letter by the way. Best letter I ever had, especially the bit about old Uncle Ralph giving your Nurse Roundway a tweak. Sounds as if he's well in there! Like the bit about 'Eden Blighted – the one who wrote the Neurotic Nine books' as well. Something tells me I'd get on really well with your father – which reminds me, I'm not one of your get-up-at-dawn-and-pray-for-three-hours types, but I have been flicking the odd tiddly-wink up towards Holy Head Office. So have lots of others, so we'll probably see a bit of action in that area before long. Get in touch with old Father John – pure gold, he is. Talking about fathers – dear old Dad (the fascist, you know) is his same old loony self. Dad's pure gold in his own way as well, but he does get himself into some scrapes. The other day my cousin Wanda rang to ask if we could look after her babies for one night. Oh, Andy Pandy, you should see 'em! Triplets – three boys, one year old, and their names are Shadrach, Meshach, and Abednego. Their dad's a Christian steelworker, so he's really into fiery furnaces. Anyway, Mum was out when the call came, so Dad took it, and his end of the chat went something like this.

'Hello, Wanda . . . yes, I see . . . yes, I understand . . . yes of course it's an emergency, I can see that . . . just for the Friday night? . . . oh, yes! No problem . . . of course I mean it. We adore children . . . no it's not Wanda, it's nothing at all. You just go ahead and make the arrangements and don't even think about Friday night . . . no, it's a pleasure *really*. I'll enjoy it . . . Yes . . . 'bye Wanda.'

All through the call I was trying to attract Dad's attention, Andy, but he kept waving me away like he does when he gets exasperated. So after he'd put the phone down he turned to me and started ticking me off.

'I should have thought,' he said, all dignified, 'that it might be possible to speak on the telephone in my own house' (he only owns about one brick, Andy) 'without my son waving like a dervish at me because he can't wait to make some totally irrelevant comment!'

'Sorry, Dad,' I said, 'I was just trying to tell you that . . .'

Mum came through the door just then and asked what was going on. So Dad explained, still very dignified, and when he got to the bit about me trying to interrupt, she just leaned back against the door and started giggling.

'I wasn't aware,' said Dad, 'that anything I've said is particularly amusing.'

'No, it's not really, darling,' said Mum, 'it's just that I think what Gerald was trying to say to you was that I'm not actually here on Friday night, am I? Remember? I promised I'd stay with Samantha Rind-Smythe for the night, didn't I, sweetheart?'

Poor old Dad went all white and quivery, Andy, and he made a little screaming sound in his throat. He tried to 'unfix' it with Wanda, but she wasn't in when he phoned back, and he knew she'd have made all her arrangements by the time he could get in touch with her.

So there we were Friday evening, Mum away till the next morning, and Dad, wild-eyed but determined, doing a real Forth Bridge job on Shadrach, Meshach and Abednego. I think Dad was actually getting to quite like them after a while, except for Abednego perhaps. Abednego really does look incredibly like Bernard Manning, Andy, and his sense of humour isn't much different. He threw his jelly and cream all over Dad, then laughed and clapped.

Anyway, by ten o'clock Shadrach and Abednego were asleep, but Meshach had decided he wanted a long and important chat with Dad. He waved his little arms around and babbled away for ages (just like some of the people in our church), and Dad sat, a bit pop-eyed with tiredness, and listened to him.

'Do you think he's really saying something?' asked Dad after a while.

'Yes,' I said, 'I think he's trying to give you a message – something from scripture, I expect. In fact, I think I can interpret what he's saying.'

Old Dad's just a little bit easy to play jokes on, Andy Pandy. I got a piece of paper, wrote on it, put it in an envelope, sealed it up and handed it to Dad.

'Here you are, Dad,' I said, 'this is the verse I think he's trying to say to you. You open it in the morning and I bet you find it's an accurate prophecy.'

Dad said tiredly, 'Don't be silly, Gerald', but he put the envelope in his pocket, and I went off to bed.

You should have seen Dad when I came down the next morning, Andy. He looked like a dead walrus. Shadrach, Meshach and Abednego were cackling and chattering and crawling and dribbling all over him.

'Good night, Dad?' I said.

Poor old Dad was just a grey lump with a grey voice.

'No, Gerald,' he said faintly, 'I did not have a good night. I had a very bad night. I had an awful, dreadful, appalling night. Meshach continued to talk to me for the entire night, his conversation interrupted only by two dirty nappies. Shadrach had a wet nappy at one o'clock and needed a bottle at three-thirty, and Abednego had two dirty nappies, three wet ones and a screaming fit. They have *all* been awake since five o'clock and if you make any jokes I am going to kill you.'

'Of course I won't make any jokes, Dad,' I said soothingly, 'but aren't you going to look at Meshach's prophecy?'

Dad looked at me with narrowed, bleary eyes for a moment, then dragged the envelope from his pocket and tore it open.

'Go on, Dad,' I said, 'read out what Meshach was trying to say to you last night.'

Dad screwed his eyes up, then read out loud.

'One Corinthians: chapter fifteen, verse fifty-one: We

shall not all sleep, but we shall all be changed.'

Had to get out quick then, Andy Pandy, or he'd have thrown Abednego at me. I took pity on Dad after that actually. Sent him back to bed and wrestled with the terrible trio till Mum got home. Do you think he'll put it all in his precious diary? I bet he does!

Anyway, my little stretched friend, that's all for now. I'll be along later in the week, and I'm afraid I *have* bought you a dolly. I hope you don't mind.

Love, Gerald.

P.S. I've got a puzzle for you! Whose name is this an anagram of?
'LOVE AND A DREAM'

P.P.S. An anagram is when you mix the letters up, but I expect you know that, you clever girl.

Dear Geruld,

     I have werked it owt.
Love and a dream is an dnnnagr-
amm of Adam Ovalender!

        L. B's
          Andromeda

Dear Andy Pandy,

Good try – Wrong! Try again . . .

Love, Gerald.

Dear Farther John,

I know you are a halibut nunk, but is it aul right for small girls with broke lemurs who are attractions in hosspittall to write to you? Do you live in a nunkery? Are you aloud to talk? If you aren't you ort to get a personnel problem like my frend Geruld. They don't harf pass the time if you're horizontall or not aloud to talk. I was going to be a none wonce, but farther laughed and said I'd never get into the habit. Why is that funny? I am only a small size.

Ennyway, I've got some cwestions to ask you abowt God and things. Gwenda said that relijun is the opeeum of the masses, and farther said is that why Roaming Catlicks look so glassy-eyed in church? Muther used to say prairs with me, but lately Gwenda's read me bits by sumone cauled Mouse A. Tongue at bedtime from sumthing cauled the little read book. I'm not surprised it's a little read book, Father John. I'd have more fun cuddling up with my poo like Nurse Roundway's dissgusting little neece.

Anne Plass says Jesus is allready here but I am not so shore unless he's dissgised as Mister Blogg, the porter. I hope not. Mister Blogg is a very windy person and spits in those little paper bags on the wall when Nurse Roundway's not looking. I wood be a bit dissappointid if that turned out to be Jesus, woodn't you Farther John?

Here are my cwestions.

Who made God?

Where is God?

Where is hevven?

Why didn't he stop my lemur braking?

Why dussn't he bring muther back from the green and common wimmen when I arsk him?

Where is farther?

Why dussn't he bring him when I arsk?

Can I have some chocklit soon?

Will Germain Greer get in?

What was the R101? (Farther said Gwenda made it look like a chippolarter and she was a much greater disarster).

When will I stop being an attraction?

Do you still go to hevven if yor glad your muther cried? (Don't tell God I arsked that one for goodness sake!)

Logical bonds to aul in
the Nunkery,

Andromeda Veal

P.S. Is the cheef nunk cauled a costello?

My dear Mizz Veal (may I call you Andromeda?),

I can honestly say that I have never enjoyed reading a letter more than I enjoyed reading yours. I took it into breakfast with me and laid it beside my boiled egg so that I could enjoy it in peace. We are not allowed to speak at breakfast, so I nearly got told off by the chief nunk (who certainly ought to be called a Costello, even if he isn't), because I kept chuckling over the wonderful things you wrote. We halibut nunks need all the smiles we can get, so I am very grateful to you. Life at the nunkery can be a little quiet at times, although the other brothers are all very nice. By the way, dear Anne Plass did telephone me a few days ago to say that you were in hospital after a nasty accident, so I was planning to come and see you at the same time as I visit my cousin Pearl, who has just had a little baby called George. Would you like me to bring George to see you when I come? As I expect you know, we halibuts don't usually do much marrying and having babies, so I would just love to come and show George off to you as if he were my very own, instead of being a beloved little nephew. Please let me do that.

Now, as to your questions – oh, Andromeda! I felt quite frightened. Such good questions, and so many of them! We nunks are supposed to know all about these things, but I just sat shaking my head and feeling silly. Then Brother Wilf, who is very old with two little tufts of white sticking-up hair, asked me what was the matter. I said that a young friend had written to ask me some very difficult questions about God, and I wasn't sure of the answers.

'Down to the lake, Brother John!' he said. 'Walk down to the lake and see what you find. I will attend to your duties. Away with you!'

One day, Andromeda, Brother Wilf will turn into a bright smile and just float away to heaven.

Down to the lake I went, to see what I would find. I do hope you will be able to see the lake near our nunkery when your leg is better, Andromeda. It is a shining, peaceful thing surrounded by all sorts of trees, and there is a soft quiet path running all the way round so that you can walk and walk until you come back to the place where you started. Here is a secret, Andromeda – just between you and I – sometimes I *skip* along that path. Yes! Can you imagine it – me, in my long brown habit, skipping along like some silly old sheep who's forgotten he's not a lamb any more?

Anyway, I walked along for a bit, listening to all those tiny lapping sounds you hear near lakes, until I came to one of my special places where an old wooden platform pushes out through the reeds into clear water. I stood right at the edge of the jetty, folded my arms in the big sleeves of my cloak and had a little conversation with God. I've put down what we said as though it was a sort of play. FJ is me by the way, Andromeda.

FJ: (Trying to feel holy and good) God, I have some questions . . .

GOD: (Interrupting) Look at that little coot among the reeds, John. Look at his little white face. I expect he's looking for some food. I made him, you know. What do you think?

FJ: Very nice, God – very nice, but these questions.

GOD: (Interrupting again excitedly) John! John! Look what's coming down the bank towards us. It's Mother Goose with her old man and all the kids. Look how she's nagging away at them from the back. Aren't you glad you're a halibut? Look how the fluffy children are marching along in line minding their P's and Q's. Dad's got his head down, John. He's having a hiss at you, warning you not to start any aggro. Better not start any aggro, John. No joke, a goose peck. Oh, those babies are so pretty! Not bad, eh, John?

FJ: *Very* attractive, God. Very nice, but . . .

GOD: (Sounding a little sad) Oh, John, you should have seen it in the beginning! It was so lovely. It will be again one day too. That's exciting isn't it, John? Isn't it?

FJ: It's very exciting, God, of course it is. God, about Andromeda . . .

GOD: (He does interrupt, doesn't he?) John, have you ever made a goose?

FJ: Err . . . no, God.

GOD: Have you ever built a coot, John?

FJ: No, God, I've never built a coot.

GOD: Well, let *me* tell *you* that making coots and geese is very complicated. Helping Andromeda is a piece of cake compared with building a coot. You go and tell her I love her very much, and she'll get all her answers as time goes by. I'm working on it right now. You will tell her, won't you, John?

FJ: Yes, God, I will tell her.

Look out for me and George, Andromeda. You should be able to tell us apart. We're both bald, but he dribbles more than me.

God bless from all at the nunkery,

Father John.

P.S. Why don't you write a letter to God? I do sometimes.

Dear Geruld,
            Gott it! It's Mad Ronald
Eave.
                L. B's

                Andromeda

Dear Andromeda,

Wrong again! Here's a clue. Love and a dream is an anagram of the name of someone I like very much. Good luck!

Love, Gerald.

Dear Mister Pluckley-Turf,

I got yor name from somone in the hospittal where I am a long-term attraction since the old lemur bitt the dust. Being horizontall doesn't mean you carn't have vertical opinions you gnow, and seeing as you are our local ~~repri repp repree repperez~~ m. p. I thort I'd write you a greevance about the Natural Health Surface in jeneral. and this hosspitall in paticular. My frend Gerald (he has kindley donated his persunnel problem for hosspittal use) says that even though I am a left-leaning red person and you are a blue Thacher-scratcher, you still have to lissen to me becos I'm one of your constititituents. I may be onley eight now, but in ten yeers I shall be aloud to vote, eh, Pluckley-Turf, old man? If you want to be ~~a~~ miniskirt of health and soshul obscuritee one day you'll need all the votes you can gett!

Ennyway! It's about Nurse Roundway who looks arfter me. She is very
round and kined and smiles a lot,
but the uther day she was crying in
the nite when she thort I was
asleep, and I arsked why and she
jumped like a ambushed beachball
and told me it was becos she is
verry tired becos there is lots to do
and not enough nurses to do it and
she tries to do more but carn't
and she's sad becos peeple arn't
getting lookt after like thay
should. Then she made a beamy
smile come on her face and said
she was being silly and making a
fuss like a stewpid old woman and she
playd three littal words with me til
I dropt off.

All you've got to do, Mister Pluckley - Turf is stand up in the
House of Comments and say that
Nurse Roundway cried and then
everyone will undastand and Mrs.
Thacher will tell the civil serpents
to give all the hospittalls some
more money and all the Nurse

Roundways will be orlright again. I bet you carn't wait to stand up and get it all sorted out, eh? I bet Mrs. Thacher'll line up something really speshul for you after that!

You do think Nurse Roundway's hosspittal <u>should</u> have more money, don't you, Mr. Pluckley Turf?

Reguards

Andromeda Veal (Mizz)

Dear Ms Veal,

Rest assured that the issue raised in your letter of last week, is one which has received, and will continue to receive, attention commensurate with the importance attached to it by we whose responsibility it is to consider such matters in the interests of those who ultimately hold us accountable for such consideration, whoever and wherever they may or may not be. You ask me to state unequivocally my view on whether the hospital in which you are at present situated should receive an increased budget for staffing purposes, and perhaps it is your view that politicians are incapable of giving a straight answer to a question. That suggestion I must reply to by answering your question with a resounding proviso. In my own case I think I can honestly say that I have never failed to provide for those upon whom it is incumbent to take responsibility for the elicitation of appropriate responses from persons such as myself in the case of issues such as the one we are addressing, a statement of personal policy which, in terms of specific and unprejudiced concentration on aspects which by their very nature demand totally unbiased and quite unambiguous judgement, are, in a variety of non-discriminatory ways, quite singularly oriented.

Now, to the actual circumstances pertaining to your individual environmental situation. Should the hospital in question receive extra funding for staff? I can assure you, Ms Veal, that I shall not be found guilty of that iniquitous obfuscation which invariably characterises the type of spurious response that we who humbly yet steadfastly adhere to a species of communication that cannot be described in other than superlative terms with regard to straight-forwardness and regard for what in the circumstances I am bound to refer to as the truth, have come to anticipate in a non-condemnatory but vigorously objective way, from those of our opponents who might be felt possibly to be verging on the brink of the hint of a tendency to be otherwise than open in their statements.

I hope I make myself clear.

None of us can afford, whatever our personal political and social persuasions and inclinations, to ignore the issue of staffing needs in those establishments which in time of physical and mental need carry out their statutory duties as representatives of the corporate will of the British tax-paying public in respect of necessary treatment of that aforementioned need. I reject and abhor such an attempt to side-step the responsibility for close and careful examination of such a complex and, in the atmosphere of negative and therefore potentially positive growth and prosperity prevalent at this time, purely indistinct issue as this one, which it behoves every one of us to face and explore with courage, whatever the outcome may be.

I am personally willing to exercise every ounce of energy and influence that I possess in a fully committed act of restraint with regard to unqualified acceptance of any view which does not fully comprehend the complexities of a position diametrically or obliquely opposed to such a view, and I am in total accord with those who, while decrying unconsidered allegiance to one opinion or another, are prepared to give their whole-hearted support to the proposition of retreat from acquiescence in the suggestion of any failure to act dynamically.

Need I say more? You may be sick in our hands with total confidence.

Yours faithfully,

Hugh Pluckley-Turf.

P.S. The Roundway employee whom you mention is, like all other National Health employees, entitled to days off in lieu of extra hours worked. With a little organisation she will have no further grounds for complaint. The system caters for her type of situation. Need I say more?

Dear Mister Pluckley-Turf,

Eh?

Yours facefully

Andromeda Veal (Mizz)

P.S. After reeding your bit about Nurse Roundway I looked up the end bit of your name in the dick-shunnary. It said turf is the same as another werd that starts with S and ends with D.
Need I say moor?

Dear Young Person,

(I think it best not to use your first name as I sense occult and astrological connotations in the term. Have mother and father dabbled? My anointed spouse, Stenneth and I have a special ministry in this area, not least because Stenneth, as a young person, unredeemed and adhering to the natural, was exposed to his grandfather's card trick. Thankfully, he is now released, but it is a lesson to us all).

Your name and needs were passed to us by a friend of Anne Plass, with whom I believe you are corresponding. I am surprised that Anne failed to mention it to me herself so that Stenneth and I could offer immediate ministry. But that is so like *dear* Anne. So gloriously human, and so devoted to her husband, who is certainly *not* retarded in my view, and her son Gerald, for whom we pray constantly, that his flippancy and lack of respect will be dealt with in the fullness of time. Only last week he referred to our new assistant Elder, a tall red-haired man with a habit of blinking hard every few seconds as the 'belisha deacon'. I am sorry to report that the majority of the house group seemed to find this remark highly amusing. I prayed silently for those present, and Stenneth's outrage was such that he suffered a choking fit and was forced to leave the room. However, I do not judge Gerald. God will do that.

Now to your accident. I wonder, dear, if there is some little naughty in your life that needs to be brought under the blood. I recall an incident some months ago when Stenneth fell from the loft after climbing the ladder to procure an article for me. He had maintained that the ladder was in such a state of disrepair that it would not support his weight. I agreed therefore, to stand at the bottom of the ladder and prevent the rungs from breaking by faith. As he lay on the landing floor, moaning and clutching the base of his spine, I asked *him* if there was some little unconfessed sin in his life that was gently being pointed out to him. At that instant, before my very eyes, Stenneth was possessed by a spirit of uncontrollable anger, coming very close to a physical attack on my person, shouting as he did so that the only mistake he had ever made was taking advice from 'cabbage-headed idiots who were about as spiritual as mud'. (I thought this a little hard on your Uncle Edwin, who, while not fulfilling the scriptural criteria for eldership totally, tries to do his best.) Despite Stenneth's denial, however, I was not at all surprised when, later in the day, secreted under Stenneth's portion of the nuptial mattress, I discovered an issue of a certain magazine which deals with the construction of balsa wood aeroplanes, an area wont to hold Stenneth captive in the natural, and one which he abandoned after it was

revealed to me that if the number of letters in 'balsa wood' is multiplied by the age at which my saintly second cousin Maud's father died, namely 74, the resultant total is 666, the number of the 'Beast'. It was clear to me, then, on discovering this publication, that Stenneth had been covertly feasting his eyes on illicit constructional illustrations and that his fall from the loft was a call to repentance.

So, young person, *is* there a little knot in the string of your life? If so, you must unpick it and make sure you keep your string nice and tight in future.

I have told Stenneth it is his duty to write to you, and you will be excited to hear that I may be able to visit you soon. Won't that be nice?

Yours faithfully,

Victoria Flushpool.

P.S. The Plasses do *mean* well, dear.

Dear Anne,

Misses Flushpool has ritten me a pecewlier letter that I don't rearly undastand. Will you look at this coppy of the letter. I have ritten back and tell me if you think it's aul right? She fritens me a bit.

Dear Misses Flushpool,
I am not shore from your letter if you are narsty or nice. Witch? I arsk myself. I don't know why you say narsty things about my frend Geruld. If it wosn't for his persunnel problem I wood be bawd out of my mined. Wood you lend sumone _your_ persunnel problem if they were horizontall in sum way? Arsk yorself _that_ ~~quest~~ Misses Flushpool, eh? (Have you got a persunnel problem by the way? If you havn't you ort to go down the shop and say to the man — show me yor persunnel

74

problems because I want one if they don't cost two much).

Annother thing — Geruld feels sorry for you, Misses Flushpool. When I staid with the Plasses I heard him say to the fashist that he thort you had a miserable old face ache. He caired about you being in payne, Misses Flushpool! And he told Anne how well ejucated you are. You must be very prowd of yor deegree in hipockrusee. Anne got mad with Geruld when he said that for sum reeson, but she smyled when he'd gone out of the room. Groan ups are a bit odd if you arsk me.

I am afrayed I ~~did~~ diddn't undastand a lot of yor letter, but you did arsk if my muther and farther had ever dabbled. I don't cwite see what it's got to do with you, Misses Flushpool, but if you must gnow, they did dabble wonce when we were on holiday in Brighten. Farther roled his trowsers up and muther helld her skert up (you coold see her nickers

, Misses Flushpool!) and they jumpt about on the edge of the sea. They were cwite happy then but when they went back the next yeer muther met Gwenda and it aul startid going wrong. Farther hates Brighten now. He says you have to be a feemale, marxist, homersexyouall, hunchbacced dworf with a percycution complecks if you want to fit in at Brighten. It must be a very funny plaice. I thort it was just seaside.

I remember yor husband Stenneth, Misses Flushpool. He is a smaul man who only says Amen to that and looks sadd when nowone's wotching. Has he got a big probblim of some sought? Tell him to get Geruld to tell him sum of his jokes. There rearly funny, they are.

Ennyway, Misses Flushpool, thats aul for now. Keep yor pecker up, as farther says.

reguards

Andromeda Veal (Mizz).

P.S. Wots so wrong with my name? It's betta than being naymed after a raleway stashun like you; eh?

Well their it is, Anne. Wot do you think? She'll think a bit diffrunt abowt Geruld arfter that, eh? Perhapps she'll arsk him to tea or sumthing. I'll post it off to her twomorrow.

Logical bonds,

Andromeda.

Dear Anne,

Gosh, I was rearly suprised when Nurse Roundway came over this mourning and said you had just phoned to say doan't send that letter to Misses Flushpool. She said you sownded as if you were a bit hett up. I was just abowt to hand it in to be poasted, Anne. It's a pity rearly because I addid on a bit abowt when Geruld said that when God gave out chinns, Misses Flushpool thort he said gins and awdered a dubble. Woodn't she have larfed, Anne? Pleese let me gnow wot was wrong with sending it. I mite have cheered her up, eh?

Logical bonds

Andromeda.

(PR 19:15) (HOS 9:1) (JOHN 5:39) (ACTS 19:9)

Deep Joy Bible School
(MAT 7:14)—Narrowpath Road—(I SAM 27:10)
Dumpton
Wessex

(JER 31:20)

Dear Andromeda,

I (GEN 6:17, EX 3:11, LEV 26:28, NUM 3:12, DEUT
7:17, JOSH 14:7, JUDG 5:3, I SAM 24:17, II SAM 3:28,
JOB 1:15, EZRA 7:21, NEH 5:15, ESTH 4:16, PS 61:2,
ECCL 2:25, HEB 2:13, REV 1:17, ISA 44:7, MAT 18:20)
will (DEUT 21:14, JOB 13:13, PR 21:1, DAN 4:17, MAT
8:3, MARK 1:41, LUKE 5:13, MAT 20:15, MARK
14:36, JOHN 18:39, MARK 6:25, LUKE 4:6, JOHN
5:21, ACTS 18:21, ROM 7:18, I COR 4:19, PHIL 2:13,
TIT 3:8, JAS 4:15, REV 11:6, DAN 4:35, COL 1:9) **pray**
(GEN 20:7, I SAM 7:5, II SAM 7:27, EZRA 6:10, I KI
8:30, I CHR 17:25, NEH 1:6, JOB 21:15, PS 5:2, ISA
16:12, JER 7:16, ZECH 7:2, MAT 5:44, LUKE 16:27,
MAT 6:5, MARK 13:18, ROM 8:26, PHIL 1:9, HEB
13:18, I TIM 2:8) **for** (DEUT 4:7, II SAM 11:22, PR
28:21, MAT 5:45, JOHN 1:16, ROM 13:6, II COR 5:1, II
PET 3:12, MAT 6:7, II COR 13:8, MAT 25:35) **you**
(JOSH 3:4, JOB 16:4, ISA 59:2, EZEK 11:19, AMOS
2:13, LUKE 10:16, ROM 2:24, II COR 9:4, EPH 2:1,
COL 1:21, GEN 9:9, LEV 25:46, DEUT 11:4, I SAM
25:19, JER 42:16, II COR 9:14, PHIL 1:8, EX 10:16, LEV
26:17, JER 44:11, NUM 17:5, DEUT 1:44, JOSH 23:16,
MI 1:2) **every** (GEN 6:5, LEV 19:10, NUM 5:2, I SAM
3:18, PS 119:101, PR 2:9, ISA 45:23, ROM 14:11, JER
51:29, EZEK 12:23, DAN 11:36, ZECH 12:12, MAL

1:11, MAT 4:4, MARK 1:45, LUKE 4:37, ACTS 2:43, I COR 4:17, II COR 10:5, EPH 1:21, PHIL 2:9) **day** (GEN 1:5, EX 21:21, LEV 23:37, NUMB 3:13, DEUT 4:10, JOSH 6:10, JUDG 16:2, RUTH 4:5, I SAM 9:15, JER 15:9, NEH 4:2, ESTH 9:17, JOB 1:4, PS 19:2, PR 4:18, ISA 7:17, JER 12:3, EZEK 4:6).

Love (GEN 29:20, II SAM 1:26, PR 5:19, ECCL 9:1, JER 2:2, EZEK 16:8, DAN 1:9, HOS 3:1, MAT 24:12, JOHN 13:35, ROM 8:35, GAL 5:6, COL 1:4),

Charles

x (PR 27:6, LUK 7:45, ROM 16:16, I THES 5:26, HOS 13:2, PS 2:12)

PART III

Dear Anne,

Oh, Anne! Gess what, gess what! Farther John cayme to see me yesterday like he said he wood and gess what! He brort George (that's how you spel it, I do'nt gnow why), and gess what, Anne. George liked me, he did. He <u>did</u> Anne! His muther is cauled Pearl and she told Farther John it was orlright for me to meat George and he brort him and I did and he smiled at me and oh, Anne! Listan, Anne, do you gnow abowt baby's hands? Their very smaul arn't they? George's hands are very very very smaul and Farther John said lets tell eech other what we think his hands look lyke. He said he thort they were lyke littal tiney bunches of pealed prawns. That was pritty good, eh, Anne? I wanted to think of sumthing even betta, so I thort and thort about what George's littal fingas peeping out of his sleeves lookt lyke, and gess what, Anne! I rememberd when I went on the beech with Farther at Brighten and he picked up a incy littal shell from a rock pool and held it on his hand and said – Wotch this, Andy bugs! (Daddy ewsed to caul me Andybugs, Anne). And arfter a while sum titchy littal legs cayme creeping owt of the shell and a littal creecher walked allong Daddy's hand loocking four his home in the sea. Daddy told me it was cauled a hermitt crab, Anne. They pinch shells from wincles wile their owt.

Ennyway, I said to Farther John – I think George's fingers twiddling owt of the ends of his sleeves look just lyke a littal hemitt crab's legs comming owt of his shell. And gess what, Anne. Farther John said he thort my idear was the best! Betta than the pealed prawns! Acey-pacey skill for sumone who's a horizontall attraction, eh, Anne? Farther John said he could tell George lyked me becos he loocked at me and dribbald down his nuncles brown habbit in a happee sort of way.

Then nurse Roundway came allong and said oo isan't he sweet and things and isan't he lyke his daddy (meening Father John). So I pokt her jently in the base and wissperd — he's a halibut nunc, he lives in a nunkery. Then she notissed his habit and went aul red, but Father John said it was orlright and axshully he felt flatterned. You'd think Nurse Roundway wood have more cents, woodant you, being higlee trained and aul? She's a E. S. N., you gnow. Father John says I'm George's onararary arnt. That's eggsiting, eh?

Logical bonds,

Andromeda.

P. S. Tell you sumthing, Anne. Doon't

tell ennyone else becos it sounds
sillee, but when I was lying quiett
jus now, do you gnow whot I thor-
t? Father John onley rearly torks
about ducks and coots and babys
and things, but arfter he's gonn
it feals as if Jesus has bin.
Funny, eh?

Dear Geruld,

Gottit this thyme! The persun you like is Eva Raddlemoan!

L. B's
Andromeda.

P.S. Eva Raddlemoan's not a little girl, is she, Geruld?

Dear Andy Pandy,

Eva Raddlemoan?! You must be joking! Another clue – this person who I like VERY MUCH has got the initials AV. Come on!!!

Love, Gerald.

Dear Child,

I am a nun in the Order of Saint Bollom of Nurd. He formed his Order in 463 and entitled it The little Brothers and Sisters of Inverted Ablution. He declined all food but squirrel droppings, and believed that God is most profoundly encountered in small purple objects immersed in badger's milk. He spent most of his life under a tree with his follower, developing the tenets by which we of the Order still live.

My name by the way is Sister Valium, and I was told of your plight by a holy Father of my acquaintance. He happened to mention the name of the hospital wherein you are constrained, and I have decided to address your soul on the qualities needful to one in your position.

First, we learn of the need for Patience from Saint Hormone of Pucket, a great intellectual of the middle ages who spent his life patiently attempting to prove his contention that the world was shaped like an aardvark's pelvis. He died in 1163 when a recalcitrant aardvark aggressively resisted his research. We revere his memory and we pray with him for that same quality of patience.

For a lesson on stillness, we turn to the work of another giant of the early church, Saint Weirdlip of Grime. Saint Weirdlip was commissioned to compose a poem on stillness by Pope Verminous the 59th in 269, and I have set the finished work down here for your edification.

> Be still, and if not still,
> Still, in not still, still be still,
> Still, until still cannot be still,
> Be still, and still be still,
> In not still. Oh, be still!

Saint Weirdlip, a great traveller, read his poem every-where until his death in 274 when he fell off a pyramid. We remember his words and seek to attain that stillness.

Thirdly, we turn to Saint Gudgeon of Milton Keynes, a more recent teacher, to learn of the place in which we might find truth. Saint Gudgeon lived a hermit's life, preferring to remain in his Wendy House on the roof of a local fire station, emerging only to impart the newly ripened fruits of his long periods of meditation and contemplation. Saint Gudgeon delivered the following address to passers-by in a loud voice as they passed the fire station one Saturday morning.

'Brothers and Sisters, I tell you that when we seek the truth inside, it is actually outside, and when we look for it above, it is actually below, and when we hope to find it in front of us, it is actually behind us, and when we think we have found joy, we have actually found sadness, and when we are in turmoil, we are actually at peace, and when the wind blows, the air is actually very still, and when the rain falls it is actually very, very dry, and black is actually white, and get your hands off me . . . !'

Unfortunately, Saint Gudgeon's address was terminated by the arrival of two uniformed persons who maintained that the peace was being disturbed, and offered him the choice of quickly returning to his Wendy House or accompanying them to the police station. Enough of his homily emerged, however, for us to learn of the search for truth, and to feel grateful for the wisdom of this holy man.

So, child, may your soul benefit from these truths and may they be an aid to swift recovery.

Benedictions,

Sister Valium

Dear Sister Valium,

Thancyou four writing me aul that Sainte Bogwash stuff and that. My sole has befenittited from it. No dowt abowt that, eh? I had a Wendy house wonce becos farther bort me one, but Mother and Gwenda wood only lett me play with it if I cauled it a Willy house and put plastick Bigot inside two do the howsework, and I had to preetend to go off eech morning to do my carrear in the billding trade.

Farther got drunk once and sat innside with Bigot for hours and woodn't come owt so muther demolish-uned it aul round him and he jus sat holeding Bigot and ~~singin~~ sing-ing We shall Ovacome. That wos the end of my Willy house.

Regards to aul in the advent,

Andromeda Veal (Mizz).

Dear God,

A frend of yors cauled Father John said it wood be aul right to write to you. As you gnow (beeing omnisheeant), I am a horizontall attraction at the moment, but I hope to be A1 lemur-wise before two long. Farther John has eggsplained to me abowt Jesus and the cross and aul. He says I can be in it if I want. I want to be in it, God, but I am afrayed you will not be getting a verry good deel. I was glad when muther said she cryed. Pretty bad eh, God? Can you still have internal salvashion if yor glad yor muther cryed? Farther John said you wood forgive ennything, but nunks do get a bit carryed away, don't they? Mined you, I do understand a bit abowt Jesus on that cross becos when Farther John said abowt it, I said it was a bit like being stretched horizon-

tall like me, only up strait. He
said it was, so I said Oh, so
Jesus was rearly an attraction
like me? Then Father John's eyes
went aul wet and he said

Yes, Andromeda, he was an attraction just like you. He smiled
threw his teers, God. Does that
mean there must have been a
rainbow on my face? Next time
Farther John came too see me, he
brort me a collidoscope. It's grate
God! You look threw this incy
littal hole and their are all
shining peaces making a ~~butiful~~
butiful pattern. Farther John
said I cood be a littal shining
peace in the collidoscope that Jesus
is, so next time you look threw a
little hole at yor son Jesus yooll
gnow one of the shining peaces is
Andromeda Veal (Mizz).

Ennyway, the uther thing is, good
luck with Muther and Farther and
Gwenda. I hope you mannage to sought
it aul out. Farther John says
they aul got sum things wrong. It's

a big job for you, God. The larst
time I saw them aul togetha
was when Gwenda cut her finger
and farther ran and got a punc-
ture repare outfitt. That was the
last straw. Muther told farther
to cleer off and never come back.
    Tuff one eh, God? Betta get
an ace angel on it.
      Logical bonds,
        Andromeda Veal (Mizz)

P.S. I bleeve yor acwainted with
George, who is Farther Johns neffew.
He is a sooperconfabulus baby who
likes me.   Ennyway, sumone brort
him over two the nunkery the other
day to vizit his unncle and
Father John left him with Bruther
Wilf for a minnit while he went
sumwhere. Ennyway! When he
cayme back he said that George and
Bruther Wilf (he has too tufts of
white hare sticking up from his
head, God. Do you gnow him?) were
just smiling at eech uther and
just for a ⚡ seccond he thort they

were eggsackly the sayme age!
Silly eh, God? One's verry old
and the uthers hardly borned!

P.P.S. I've adresst this to God c/o
hevven. I hop that's aul right.

Dear Geruld,
     Alan Veedordam! Eh?

L. B's.

      Andy-pandy
(That's what <u>you</u>
   caul me, Geruld).

Dear Andy Pandy,

Can you honestly imagine me REALLY LIKING someone called Alan Veedordam? I can't even say it. I can see I'll have to give you a lot more clues. Here goes! The person whose name is an anagram of Love and a Dream is:

(1) Someone I like VERY MUCH.
(2) Someone whose initials are AV.
(3) Someone who is in hospital with a broken leg.
(4) Someone who is eight years old.
(5) Someone who wants a bad beautiful dolly.
(6) Someone who is very pretty.
(7) Someone who I'm going to give a new personal stereo to when her birthday comes.

Love, Gerald.

Worldwide Christian Entertainment Corporation
Music for Planet Earth Project
Prefab Number 3
Armistice Row
Bagshot

Telephone (Reconnection awaits faith income)

Dear Brother or Sister,

How true it is that as one door closes another one opens. We now know and believe that the Universal Conversion College Project was meant to test our faith in preparation for the REAL task, that of organising and financing massive musical outreach events throughout the known world. Sadly, one or two of our number have left on finding that our earliest prophetic word (to the effect that the College would stand and be fruitful until the second coming) is no longer intended to be fulfilled. Regretfully, the departed brethren were unable to sustain faith in our divinely inspired change of direction, and faith, after all, is what underpins and makes possible the Lord's work.

Once again we must apologise for the even poorer quality of paper and print in our newsletter, but there are insufficient funds at present to repair our duplicating machine or to purchase new stocks of paper. Once again, however, our needs have been wonderfully met. One of our number retrieved an old John Bull child's printing set from the loft in his parents' house, and incredibly, on the very same day we discovered an anonymous gift of almost fifty sub-standard brown paper bags, simply left in the middle of the road outside our prefab. Wondrous indeed! And clear evidence that we are following the correct path.

As if more evidence was needed! It is now only weeks since it was revealed clearly that the three of us who remain are to create a powerful new musical force that will completely transform the concept of Christian music around the globe. In those weeks I have almost mastered E minor and G major on my little sister's guitar, and as funds are prayed in and it becomes possible to purchase the two missing strings, I believe in my heart that I shall be able to strum a three-chord accompaniment to 'Go Tell Aunt Rhody' by the time Christmas is here. That is not ordinary progress!

Much musical equipment will be needed, including sound systems, a range of the best guitars, drums and drum machines, keyboards of every description, special lighting effect facilities, and, of course a combination of vans and Range Rovers to transport the equipment to venues all over the world. Already we have a second-hand plectrum and a skateboard. Pledges, we believe, of the abundance that is to come. Please pray that my little sister will not notice her guitar is missing until after Christmas.

More strongly than ever we believe that we are called to live and work entirely by faith, without mentioning problems and hardships that could be alleviated by financial contributions. God knows, such difficulties abound, and, if listed, would cover several paper bags, but we are confident that the necessary funds *will* arrive and, after all, what is hunger, cold, lack of clothing and discomfort at night compared with the advancement of the Kingdom? Once more we make an impassioned plea that those who feel led to spend their money on shallow personal pleasures rather than the Lord's work should feel free to do so. We really do *not* want your cheques or postal orders (crossed and made payable to the WWCEC), unless you care.

Yours,

Vernon Rawlings (sic sec)

P.S. News of musical venues will follow. Eventually we hope to perform at Las Vegas, Wembley Arena, the Shea Stadium, and in Red Square. Our only actual booking at present is Stanley (my assistant) playing the spoons at amateur night in the public bar of the Frog and Spittle just down the road from the prefab. We really are looking for a miracle here, as we possess only one spoon and Stanley has never done it before.

Dear Geruld,
        Oh, Geruld! It was me!
Oh, Geruld. Love and a dream.
Oh, Geruld!

    L. B's.

    Andromeda Veal.
      (Andy-pandy) X.

Dear Farther John,

How are you and aul the uther halibuts? How is Bruther Wilf? I have dun a pichure of him to hang on his sell door. I bet heel be the onley one in the nunkery to have an eriginal Veal. One day in the fucher they'll sell it at Smotherbee's action rooms for trillyons and trillyons of pownds, and Brother Wilf's grate granchildrun will be as rich as acey-pacey Cliff Richud. Oh no! I forgott nunks doon't have baybies, do they? Well he cood leave it too the nunkery if he wants, so they can train up new Bruther Wilfs in the fucher. I hope he lykes my pichure. I did it four him becos he did yor work for you while you torked to God abowt coots and that, down by the lapping lake.

Listan, Farther John! Gess

what's happerned! I doon't gnow
if I menshunned it too you, but
I have nevver had a dolly
eggsept plastick Bigot and he
was a vicktim of dumbestic
vilence. Gwenda said that in
the new aje arfter the reverlooshun wimmin woodn't be miss-
lead by such divices. She said
wimmen get a ror deal aul
round becos men ewes them. She
said sheed never aggree to
show her nakid body on page
threee of the tablet press, then
farther said he'd lyke to prerpose
a vote of thanks on beeharf
of aul men evvrywhere, and it
aul got a bit vilent again.
Ennyway, Muther said I
wosn't to have a dolly becos
dollys are bad and I said I
doon't wont one ennyway if
their bad. But, Father John, I
wosn't telling the trooth! Ooh
Father John, I did wont a dolly
so much! Ennyway! In a letta
to my frend Geruld (he's going

to give me my verry own ~~dolly~~
persunnel problem soon by the way)
I sought of hinted that I
woodn't mind having a dolly,
eeven though they are bad
things. Gess what! He sumhow
got the hint! I slept aul
threw viziting this morning
and when I woke up - gess what!
Their was anuther head on the pillo
necst to mine. It was a big
dolly! A dolly, Farther John!
She is luvvly and pritty and in
a bewtiful dress and their
was a note pinnd to her dress
and what do you think it said?
Are you shaking yor hed in the
nunkery and saying — no, I
doon't gnow what it said?
Are you, Farther John? I'll
tell you. It said,
    MY NAME IS LUCKY LUCY.
Then on the uther side it said
— We have called her Lucky Lucy
because we think she's very, very
lucky to belong to such a nice
little girl, from Anne, Geruld,

and the fashist.

Oh, Father John, I cuddal my Lucky Lucy aul the thyme, but cood you say to God that duzn't meen he can slip off too the lapping lake too do a bitt of coot bilding. I wont to show my Lucky Lucy to muther and farther soon.

Logical bonds to you
and Brother Wilf

Andromeda

P.S. Did you gnow that I am a nammagranamm of Love and a dream? Geruld said. Good, eh?

P.P.S. Cood you drop me a note eggsplaining the trinnity?

Dear Anne, Geruld and nice fashist,
    I found my dolly that you brort.
    I lyke her name.
    She is grate.
    How do you say thancyoo when you wont it to sound big?
    Thancyoo
    THANCYOO

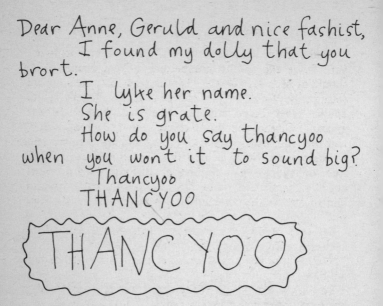

THANCYOO

Logical Bonds,

    Andy-pandy and Lucky Lucy.

P.S. Their mite be sum kissis cumming yor way when I'm verticall again.

Hi, Andy Pandy!

Glad you liked Lucky Lucy. She's a real doll, and so are you! I see the fashist has become a *good* fashist. You should've seen Dad's face when he read that. He's an old softy really. We all went to choose your dolly together, and you've never heard anything like Dad. Fussy? It was amazing! Clothes the wrong colour, ears the wrong shape, hair too long, hair too short, nothing was right. In the end he disappeared down behind this long counter to look at some dolls in boxes on the shelves. Just after he'd dropped out of sight, the lady who manages the shop came up and said to me, 'Is there something I can help you with now, sir?'

Before I could say anything, Dad's voice seemed to answer her from behind the counter.

'No! You're not pretty enough, and your knickers are falling apart!'

You know I don't get easily embarrassed, Andy Pandy, but I could feel myself going red.

'He doesn't mean you,' I said, 'he means . . .'

'As for your so-called body, it's hardly human, let alone female! Back in your box, yer ratbag!'

I explained that Dad was talking to the dolls under the counter, but that just made her very nervous instead of annoyed. Dad was mortified when he realised what had happened, so we got out quick after that and found Lucky Lucy in another shop. Your Nurse Roundway let us put her next to you while you were asleep.

Anyway! I ran into Father John yesterday on his way to speak at some meeting, and he told me you'd asked him to 'drop you a note eggsplaning the Trinity'. Good one, Andy Pandy! He was going to write back to you, but I said hold on a minute, because last Sunday we had a talk in church on the meaning of the Trinity, and I was pretty sure Dad would have got it all down in his blessed diary, especially as the 'talk' turned out to be – well, you'll see what I mean! Dad says you're very welcome to see this bit. Hope you enjoy it. I think it's *wonderful*!

Saturday

Leonard Thynn round tonight. Says he's volunteered to explain the Trinity at church tomorrow. Bit surprised really. He can hardly find his way home, let alone clarify one of the greatest theological mysteries of all. Gerald said he was looking forward to it, and did we know that theology is an anagram of 'O, get holy!'?

Sunday

Church.
Thynn started by dragging a horrible rusty old electric

fire out to the front. Plugged it into a socket at the side, then faced the congregation looking rather pleased with himself.

He said, 'Right! Trinity! Easily explained. When I switch on at the mains in a moment, I want all of you, but 'specially the children, to watch very, very closely, and see if you can spot what happens. Ready? Here we go! Keep those eyes skinned, or you might miss it!'

Suddenly felt glad I was sitting at the back. When Thynn pushed the switch down there was a loud bang and a shower of sparks. Leonard screamed and stumbled back into Doreen Cook's lap. Several children put their hands up.

Little Dotty Rawlings called out, 'I saw, I saw! It blowed up and frightened you! Is that what the Trinity means Mr Thynn?'

Leonard got up and faced us again. Looked rather white and his hair was sticking up on end. He said, 'Sorry about that, everybody. Little light should have come on, and I was going to say that was like Jesus, and then I was going to say that the electricity was like the Holy Spirit, and then . . . well, never mind. Hang on . . . !

Dashed over to the side and came back with an ancient old hoover. Switched the mains switch off, unplugged the electric fire, and plugged in the hoover. Dotty Rawlings leaned forward excitedly. Everyone else ducked.

Leonard said, 'Right! Another idea of mine – really explains the Trinity. Ready, children? When I switch on, watch what it does. Better put your fingers in your ears. Makes a bit of a racket. Here goes!'

Entire congregation flinched as Thynn switched on. Nothing at all happened. Children's hands went up again.

'It doesn't work!' squeaked Dotty Rawlings. 'The Trinity doesn't work, does it, Mr Thynn?'

Leonard turned the hoover upside down and stared sadly at it. He said, 'Hmm . . . I *was* going to say that it sweeps as it beats as it cleans, and that's a bit like the old Trini –'

Mrs Flushpool rose like an iceberg to interrupt, 'That is the mediaeval heresy of modalism, Mr Thynn!'

'No,' said Thynn, poking absently at the machinery with

his finger, 'I think it's just a coin stuck in the whatsit.'

Leonard ran out of appliances at this point so we went on to the choruses ...

Monday

Thynn round for coffee tonight, also Frank Braddock, our neighbour. Told Frank about yesterday and asked him how *he* would explain the Trinity.

He lit his pipe and said, 'You know, there are four things I like about the Trinity. First, I love having a father in God. Second, I love having a friend and brother in Jesus. Third, I love having a comforter and guide in the Holy Spirit. And fourth ...'

Anne and I said, 'Yes?'

'Fourth, I love the fact that it's a mystery. God in three persons. Three persons – one God. It's a mystery and I love it. Why would I want to spoil things by trying to explain it?'

'Mmmm ...' muttered Thynn, who wasn't listening, 'maybe if I'd used an automatic toaster ...'

Great, eh, Andy Pandy? Isn't Leonard wonderful! See you soon – love to Lucky Lucy.

Gerald.

Pope John Pall,
The Fattycan,
Roam,
Italy.

Dear Pope,
        Aul right so I'm knot a
roaming catlick, but befor you
rush off to give an ordinance to
sumone in annother part of the
Fattycan just considder this. I
have got a frend called Farther
John who is as big a halibut as
you are and I bet he gets inter-
upptid by God near gooses and
coots just as mutch as you do.
(My name is Mizz Andromeda Veal
by the way. I am horizontall
till the lemur recuvvers).
        Our cherch is not cwite like
yors, Pope. We do not have trainsin-
substandardstations at our commy-
union, we aul come in cars, but
we do have the same things to eat
and drink as yor lot, only littal
mingy bits tho, and letts face
it   Pope, the persunn in charje

of our cherch duzzn't faul
flat on his face evvery time he
steps off an airyplane like you
do. Carn't we aul joyne together,
Pope. We cood ion out our
diffrunces. For instans, you say
babies have got to be abul to do
the limbo to get into hevven.
Isn't that a bit unfare, Pope?
Why shood littal babies have to
limbo unda the gaites. Their
too smaul to lern, I reckon. I
can't do it very well and I'm
eight! Lett's leave that won out
eh, Pope? Get all your cardigan-
s together and do a bull on
them abowt it. I'm shore aul
the uther roaming catlicks will
aggree with you. In retern we
coold say you doan't have to
climb the thirty nine steps to
wear an angular preest's hood.
Fare? I think so. By the way,
isn't their one of your monseenyers
who goes on abowt crude rissoles
like the green and common
wimmen. He mite gnow my muther

and her frend Gwenda. I havn't
seen my muther since I started
being an attraction but Father
John has had a werd with God
about it and its aul in hand.
He's a nunk you see Pope.
Hears to yunitty!

Andromeda Veal (Mizz)

P.S. I hear you are a bitt of a
poet, Pope. Well, hears a coinside-
nse — so am I!!! I have writed a
poem speshully for you.

I'm not a roaming catlick,
And I sinseerly hope,
That lodes of preying cardigans,
Will never make me Pope.

I doan't think I'm a anglian,
I'd hayte to wear a hassock,
Or be like Rabbit Runcie,
And gneel apon a cassock.

I gnow who startid metherdists,
John Wesslee did of corse,

113

But I'm no good at showting,
And I cannott ryde a hoarse.

I doont think I'm a batpist,
I even hayte the rain!
When they poosh me in the warter,
Will I come upp againe?

I cood go to a howse church,
But I am rather bad,
At looking verry happy,
When I am fealing sad.

Why doon't we start a nue ~~chur~~
cherch, Pope,
Where evvrything is reel?
I've eeven got a nayme for it—
The cherch of John Paul Veal.

Aperson.

PART IV

Dear Andromeda,

My name is Frank Braddock. I live next door to Adrian and Anne Plass who I know are good friends of yours. Another person we are both friendly with is Father John. Years and years ago, we were at school together, although in those days we called each other by nicknames. His was Bungles, and mine was Smelly! You'll never guess why I was called Smelly, and I'm sure as eggs not going to tell you. The only smelly thing about me now (I hope!) is my pipe. I've found some delicious black-cherry scented tobacco, and I must admit it is rather powerful stuff. I don't think they'd want it stinking out the wards at this hospital you've landed yourself in.

Now, the reason I've written is to pay back a favour. You don't even realise you've done me a favour, do you? Well you have, and I'll tell you what it was. When you came to stay with the Plasses some months ago, you went to church with them and, although I go somewhere else usually, I just happened to be at their church on that particular Sunday. Your Uncle Edwin invited me along I think. Halfway through the service you stood up on your chair when the organist struck up, and sang 'SHE IS LORD . . .' at the top of your voice. Then the organist fellow panicked and went into 'Home, home on the range', and all was chaos. Well, ever since then, whenever I've felt a little low, I think of that day, and the organist's face, and one or two folk with their arms in the air singing ' . . . where the deer and the antelope play . . .', and I just can't stop a little chuckle from tickling its way up from inside me somewhere and forcing its way out through a smile. So thank you very much for giving me a way to cheer myself up, and that's what I'm paying you back for.

Right! So what am *I* giving *you*? Not much I'm afraid.

I'm going to tell you a story. That's my job you see – trying to write things that other people might want to read. I asked Bungles – I mean Father John – if he thought it was a good idea, and he said yes, he thought you would be good at reading stories. (He asked me, by the way, to say that the halibut nunk sends all his logical bonds). Now, here's the story. Hope you enjoy it!

Once upon a time, in a world almost exactly like ours, but with an extra thimbleful of opportunity for strange and exciting things to happen, there lived a little girl in a tall brown house. Now, I know there is nothing wrong with the colour brown. Chocolate ice-cream is dark, tasty brown, Hair can be a lovely shining brown. Some people have warm brown skins. Conkers, chestnuts, horses, birds, new shoes and little girls' eyes can all be brown and beautiful. I know that. But the house that this little girl lived in was a quite different kind of brown. It was a dead, hopeless, given-up sort of brown, an embarrassed, dingy, never-was-smart brown, and it was everywhere. I expect, when I say it was everywhere, you don't really think I mean it, do you? You think that there must have been a few yellows, a patch of red here and there, one or two orange things perhaps, some pictures on the wall with bright colours shining against the dull brownness, and, of course, whole expanses of blue sky and maybe green grass to be seen through the windows, not to mention the faces of all the people who lived in the tall brown house. Their faces can't have been that horrible brown colour, you're thinking. I tell you it was *everywhere*!

Walls, ceilings and floors – brown. Pictures, ornaments, furniture, curtains, lampshades, light bulbs, carpets, books, cups, saucers, plates, bowls, knives, forks – all brown. There might very possibly have been eggshell blue skies, and emerald lawns on the other side of the windows, but it was impossible to tell because every pane of glass was heavily tinted in one overwhelming colour – brown. There was a bird in a brown cage. He was a parrot. He ran up and down his brown ladder, looked at his brown face in his brown shaded mirror, pecked brown seed from the brown sandpaper on the floor of his cage, and had learned to say only one thing – 'Brown Polly! Brown Polly! Brown Polly!' Even the water that ran from the brown taps was brownish. It was used to make brown squash and brown tea, and brown coffee and brown Andrew's liver salts. Please believe me when I say that *everything* was brown. Brown, brown, brown, brown, brown! It was all – brown!

Now here's an embarrassing thing. I've just remembered that one thing wasn't brown. It was a book. It was the little girl's most secret and most precious thing, and she hid it very, very, very carefully in a brown space underneath the brown wardrobe where her brown clothes hung. She'd found it one day right at the back of the big bookcase in the sitting room, and when she opened it, it was as though someone had suddenly punched a book-sized hole through one of the brown-tinted windows. The colours seemed to fly up and dance around in front of her face like music that you could see. She felt quite light-headed and dizzy after only a few seconds, and had to shut the book quickly for fear of falling down. She didn't tell her mother and father about her find. She guessed somehow that they would take it away from her if they knew. So she carried it quickly up to her room and pushed it beneath the wardrobe. Every day since then, when the coast was clear, she had knelt down on her bedroom carpet, slid her hand into the secret space, and, with a little fluttery tickling feeling in her tummy, drawn out the book and feasted her eyes on the bright pages. For a long time that was enough. Just to know that brown was not all was a thrilling secret, but as the weeks went by, and the little girl grew older, she knew that she would have to sit her Mother and Father down one day and ask them to explain their brown attitudes.

The day came. Mother and Father were sitting in their brown armchairs in the brown sitting-room drinking brown drinks from brown glasses. Father was wearing a brown suit. Mother was wearing an old brown artist's smock over a pair of brown jeans. The little girl, whose name was Tanya, came into the room holding something behind her back.

'Mother and Father,' she said, 'I have a question to ask you.'

Father looked at her brownly. He had a thick brown moustache, long brown sideboards, and thin brown straggly hair. When he wasn't completely happy he rubbed at the side of his nose with his thumb. He was doing it now.

'Ask your question, Tanya,' he said. 'I will try to answer it.'

'Why is everything brown?' said Tanya, quietly and seriously.

Father laughed a clockwork laugh.

'That is not a real question,' he said. 'That is like saying, "Why has everyone got two legs?" Everything is brown because everthing is brown. That is the way it is – brown.'

'Is there only brown?' whispered Tanya.

'Yes,' said Father stiffly.

Mother looked worried.

'Why am I not allowed to see through the door when you open it? Why don't we ever open the windows? When am I going to go outside? Why have you told me fibs? Look!'

Tanya swung the open book from behind her back and held it out (open at the most colourful page) towards Mother and Father. Mother gave a little scream and put her hand over her mouth. Father stood up as though a spring had exploded in the armchair and shot him to his feet.

'WHERE DID YOU GET THAT?' he shouted.

'It's mine,' said Mother in a small wavery voice, 'I had it when I was a little girl.'

'I found it,' said Tanya. 'It's not brown. Why didn't you tell me the truth?'

'We thought it best,' said Mother tearfully. 'Colours can be dangerous.'

'Brown is safe,' said Father. 'It is our sort of colour. We did it for you. Why should you be confused by reds and blues and greens and golds and yellows and purples? We

122

had big, big problems, all because of colours. We want you to stay in a brown world and not worry. Outside is a colour jungle. Stay in and tell yourself that all you need is brown.'

'No!' said Tanya, 'I am allowed to be confused too! I *want* to go in the jungle! I *hate* brown! Open that big window!'

She pointed towards the big brown-tinted French windows. All her life they had been closed. Outside, brown flowers bloomed sadly beside brown grass under brown trees as they had always done.

'If you don't open that window *now*,' said Tanya firmly. 'I shall shut my eyes and never, never open them again!'

Mother and Father looked at each other.

Father rubbed his nose *very* hard with his thumb.

'Shall I?' he said.

'Yes,' said Mother.

Father walked over and forced the rusty old brown bolts back. He pushed the windows open. The room was flooded with light and colour. As Father stepped back Tanya ran to the open space and gazed with bright excited eyes at this dazzling world she had never seen. Looking back, she saw that Mother and Father were standing side by side, holding hands. They seemed a little bit older, and a little bit smaller, but, to her surprise, they looked a lot less brown and, for the first time for a long time, they were smiling.

God be with you, Andromeda.

Love, Frank Braddock.

Dear Cliff Richard,

Orlright so I'm onely eight and I carn't play tennis and I havun't got a exy flash nayme like Nivea Looting John, and I havun't maid records like her abowt drinking lemmonaid wen its hot cauled Let's get fizzy cool and I carn't do mutch at the moment ennyway becos I'm an ongoing attraction in hospitall until the lemur getts its akt togetha, and muther is still up with Gwenda and the green and common wimmen and aul, but why shoodun't we get marrid when I am bigger? Arfter aul, you doon't seem to get enny older. One thing tho, yew'll have to be a bit more soshulist with yor cash or Gwenda will nevver let muther let us get ingaged. And let's face it, yor pritty near a trillionair, eh? You cood have as menny personnul problems as you lyke with no cwestions arsked. It's orlright for sum!

124

My frend Geruld (doon't tell him
I've writed to you, will you Cliff?
He's seccond choise and he mite get
a bit annoyde. Gnow what I mean?)
has onley got one persunnel probbli-
m, and thats on lone to me as
long as I'm horizontall. I bet
you've gived one to Mank Harvin and
all the uther shaddoes and still
got munny over. I bet you have,
Cliff!

Lissan! Annother thing we've got
going four us, Cliff - we're both
beleevers, so it won't be a mixt mar-
rije, and you can arsk yor frend
Billee Greyham to marree us, becos
he is an ordrained batpist as long as
he isn't bizzy getting peeple up owt
of there seats at the thyme. This
necks bit took aul of yesterday to
work out, Cliff. I was abul to do it
becos of muther havving aul yor old
reccords at home. Eeven Gwenda
said that wen she was a young
gullabul girl she lyked you. She
said — he ewsed to make my legs go
all funnee — and farther said — O
125

, that's wot did it is it? — and muther tipt his bubbul and squeek down the waste dissposul.

Ennyway! Hear it is. See if yew can spot yor old reccords, Cliff.

If yew wont to go on beeing one of THE YOUNG ONES yewd betta marry this LIVING DOLL cauled Andromeda and stop beeing a BACHELOR BOY, then arfterwoods we'll go TRAVELLING LIGHT on our SUMMER HOLIDAY and if ennything getts in our way we'll MOVE IT.
Sighed,
Yor DEVIL WOMAN
Andromeda ♡

Acey-pacey skill, eh Cliffy baiby? Did you spott the songs?

Ennyway! Nurse Roundway's cumming to put powder on my base in a minnit. Horizontall = sore, Cliff! Say hallow to the shaddoes four me,
Logical Bonds

Andromeda Veal (Mizz)

P.S. Wen you were smaul, were you black with curlly hair and did you scream songs that sownded lyke Bee droppt a loofah she's my baibee or sumthin?

Dear Andromeda,

I hope you don't mind me writing you a little note. I am Lucky Wilf. I am just as lucky as the beautiful dolly that Father John has told me about, because I now have a wonderful picture on the wall of my room. A present from a little girl. Nothing could be more precious. I don't deserve to have it, but I *do* thank you for drawing it specially for me. I am very old, and not very good, but I do know that every now and then God decides that old Wilf needs a little something. *You* helped him this time. Thank you, Andromeda, so much.

Love in the name of my Master,

Brother Wilf.

Dear Bruther Wilf,

I'm pleesed you think my pichure is acey-pacey skill. Lissan! I writed a poem four the Pope the uther day, but now I want to wright one abowt baiby George for Farther John whoo's his uncel as I eggspect you gnow. I hope you ~~loll~~ do'ont mined, but I'm sending it to you to see if it's good enuff. If it's exy acey-pacey grate you can tell me it is, butt if you thinc it's pritty crabby stuff can you preetend it's not two bad but not cwite good enuff? Eh? Thancs, Bruther Wilf. Hear's the poem.

God maid George.

by
Andromeda Veal (Mizz)
Age 8

God maid George
A fat littal packit of foot on the end of eech leg,

God maid George
A smile aul cleen and speshul
   from his tummy
God maid George
Wispee moheecan hair, he's a tuffee .
   God maid George
His fisty waives say I'm alive, I am!
                                    I am!

   God maid George
No narsty bits or nauty bits he's
   onley just unpakked.
   God maid George
And he told George to smile at me, I
   nearly cryed, I did,
God maid George
      Sumtimes Georges cum owt
wrong, there braynes and boddies
         aren't maid right
   God maid _them_ two
God luvs aul _the_ Georges.

Does he luv them aul Bruther Wilf?
Not justhe aulright ones, eh?
            Logical Bonds
               Andromeda Xx

P.S.   How old _ar_ yew, for goodniss

sake?

P. P. S. I hope the kissis ar aulright four a halibut.

My dear Andromeda,

You make me feel so humble. Fancy asking *me* if I think
your beautiful poem is good enough to present to Father
John! I have not had the pleasure and privilege of meeting
little George, but after reading your poem I could almost
see him sitting in front of me, smiling and waving his fists
to show me he is 'alive – he is! he is!'. As for the 'fat littal
packit of foot on the end of each leg', oh, Andromeda, I
think that is a marvellous description. I really don't know
how you think of these things. Of *course* you must give the
poem to Father John. His eyes will light up. They do that
you know, when something special happens. I know – I've
seen them.

Andromeda, may I ask you a big favour? As you will see I
have sent the piece of paper that the poem is written on
back to you with this letter. I wonder if you would be kind
enough to give me permission to copy it out when you have
sent it to Father John? I would like to put it on my wall
beside my picture. That would be a real joy! Do say it's
alright.

You are quite right of course when you say that some
Georges – some babies – are not made right, and you asked
me if God loves them just as much. Well, I'm sure he does,
but, Andromeda, I must be honest with you. When I was a
young monk I used to get very angry indeed with God.
'Why,' I used to say, 'when you are supposed to be able to
do anything, and you are supposed to love everybody, do
you let little babies be born with things wrong with them?
Why, God? Tell me!' Oh, I *did* get ratty, Andromeda, and I
didn't seem to get any answers at all. So I went along to
someone called Brother Arnold (he was about as old then as
I am now, and much, much wiser) and told him all about it.
He listened and smiled and didn't say anything for a long
time, then he said, 'Wilf, I want you to go and kneel in the

little chapel and look at the cross on the altar, and as you kneel there I want you to say these words over and over again quite quietly to yourself—"He's in it with us—he's in it with us", then come back and tell me what you think. I'll be waiting here.'

We had a wonderful little private prayer chapel at that place, Andromeda. It was very small, not much bigger than a fairly big pantry, and there was just enough room for one person to kneel at a sort of desk thing in front of the altar. On the altar there was only a white cloth and a silver crucifix, and you had to take a candle in a brass holder from a little shelf at the side, light it with a match from the box that was always kept there, and stand it on the altar just in front and to the side of the crucifix, so that the cross was lit up by a gentle yellow glow.

That's what I did that day. Then I knelt at the desk and looked at the crucifix in front of me.

You know what a crucifix is, don't you, Andromeda? It's a cross with the figure of Jesus hanging on it. Some people don't like them. They say that Jesus rose from the dead and he's alive, so the cross should be empty. I know what they mean, and actually the big cross in the main chapel at both places where I've lived *is* an empty one, but I always thought it was right for Jesus to be there on the cross in that tiny little private chapel. I'll tell you why. You see, every day, however hard I try, I end up doing the sort of things that Jesus took the blame for on the cross. We all do. That's why he did it. He knew we'd never be good enough on our own. And every day God forgives me very enthusiastically. He says, 'Don't be discouraged, Wilf! Start again, old chap,' and I do. So you see—in a way—I put Jesus back on that horrible cross every day, and every day he dies, is buried, and rises again in me when I'm forgiven. That's why it's good to be reminded of what he did when I'm alone in the little chapel. The crucifix does that.

So, I knelt there for a while, as Brother Arnold had said I should, and repeated those words quietly and slowly, over and over again.

'He's in it with us, He's in it with us, He's in it with us . . .'

Jesus's face had been very well made by whoever modelled that crucifix. There was an expression of such pain and sweetness in his eyes, and he seemed to be looking straight at me, like those photos where the eyes follow you wherever you go in the room. And when I stopped saying those words, it was as if *he* started to speak.

'I'm in it with you, I'm in it with you, I'm in it with you . . .'

And then, Andromeda, I just started to cry. It sounds silly doesn't it, but I couldn't stop myself. The funny thing was, though, they weren't really *my* tears – they were *his*. He was showing me how *he* felt.

I went back to Brother Arnold a little later and he said, 'Well?'

I just nodded. I couldn't think what to say, and I didn't actually have any more answers than I'd had before, but I did understand that God cares for and grieves over 'the Georges that come out wrong' much much *much* more than I ever could. Beyond that it's just a mystery, Andromeda.

Try to trust Him. He adores *you*!

Love and thanks,

Brother Wilf.

Dear Andromeda,

Thynn here again – Leonard Thynn. Friend of the Plasses, remember? Sent you that hilarious – well, quite hilarious – joke about the smallish squatter behind the thingy – tree. Gottit? Good. Well, thought I'd write again with another joke – well, more an anecdote than a joke, although it's meant to *be* funny – sort of a story with a funny bit at the end, if you know what I mean.

Anyway – this joke, anecdote, or story with a funny bit at the end – tell you what – let's call it an anecdotal story with a funny bit at the end from now on just to simplify matters. Okay? Right! Where was I? Oh, yes . . . this anecdotal story with a funny bit at the end starts – well, obviously it starts, doesn't it? I mean, in a sense, as soon as you say you're going to tell it, it's already started, hasn't it, although technically it could be said to have – sorry, wittering on again. Bad habit. No problem at all after a few drinks – not that that's a good reason to drink, young Veal! Good heavens, no! Just happens to be a fact that – what was I saying? Oh, yes, of course! This anecdotal story with a funny bit at the end starts in a prison. Well, I say a prison, but I suppose it could be a detention centre, or a borstal, or (depending on the old historical perspective) a prisoner-of-war camp, or even a jolly old police cell – not that there's anything very jolly about police cells. Been in a couple I'm afraid, after getting err . . . getting err . . . arrested, as it were. No, not very jolly, but err . . . the chap in this anecdotal story with a funny bit at the end happens to be locked up in a prison, detention centre, borstal, prisoner-of-war camp or police cell, and one day he says to himself – probably not out loud – well, maybe out loud if he's been in there a long time – he says, 'I want to get out'. Sounds from that as though he's English, but actually the chap could be any nationality at all. Could be Chinese or Ukrainian or Slav or Patagonian or Scottish – mind you if he was Scottish he'd probably speak in English anyway, unless he was fanatically devoted to the re-establishment of the Gaelic language in which case he'd presumably – mind you, even if he was Chinese he might have been brought up in – say, Luton, in which case he'd probably speak English with a Chinese accent, one would guess.

Anyway, this chap in the prison, borstal, detention centre, prisoner-of-war camp or police cell, says to himself in his own particular language, accent, dialect, or patois, 'I want to get out'. And then – to cut a long story short – well, significantly shorter anyway – he says it again, and this time he really means it. Not that he didn't mean it the first time. It's just that the second time he err . . . meant it more. More than the first time, that is.

So, the chap (of uncertain nationality) digs a hole in the floor of his cell – if that's what he's in. Well, he must be in *some* sort of cell, unless he's a member of staff, in which case he wouldn't need to dig a . . . where was I? Ah, right! He digs a hole. Don't know how he does it. Not a practical chap myself. Once got Radio Four on the hoover when I was trying to fix the iron. Bit of a surprise really. Good programme though – all about the Watusi Tribe of Central Africa. Amazing people! Apparently they never, never – sorry, mustn't get side-tracked – spoils the err . . . anecdotal story with a funny bit at the end. He digs a hole, so that he can burrow out – tunnel out's better. 'Burrow' sounds a bit too rabbit-like really, don't you think? – he tunnels though the ground and comes out in the street outside. More good luck than good management, I'd say, unless he had special knowledge of the prison – which he might have done. Let's be fair! You don't get told that when you hear the joke – not that it matters – much . . .

Yes, well, anyway – he climbs out of the thingy – the hole, and he shouts out (in English or Chinese or Ukrainian or Slav or English with a Scottish accent, or Gaelic, or English with a Chinese/Luton accent) 'I'm free! I'm free!'

And then (the funny bit at the end of the anecdotal story is virtually imminent here, Andromeda), a little boy who happens to be passing—and, unless the digging chap has managed to burrow (tunnel rather) right through to another continent, he's presumably the same nationality as the digging chap—says (and this is the actual funny bit at the end of the anecdotal story) 'That's nothing—I'm four!'

Get it? 'I'm free! I'm free!' 'That's nothing—I'm four'. What a scream, eh? Well, anyway . . .

All the best, young Veal. Don't fret now. Got the boss on our side. Know what I mean? Mother sends her love by the way. Says if she can put up with me for thirty-mumble years, you'll survive your hospital experience.

Regards,

Leonard (Thynn)

P.S. When you're better, you must (well, if you want to—no 'must' about it) come round and see what I've taught the Plasses' cat to do. You'll be amazed—well, very surprised anyway . . .

Dear Andromeda,

It was with abundant joy that I received the wonderful news of your hospitalisation. How marvellous to suffer as you are doing! What a depth of gratitude and deep thankfulness you must be experiencing as you lie in the privileged position of one who is allowed to enjoy pain and discomfort hour after hour and day after day.

Hallelujah!

How you must delight in and chuckle over those verses which reveal the inestimable benefits of regular immersion in the rich baptism of physical anguish. How I envy you your glorious opportunity to participate in the ecstasy of awful agony. Oh, to break a femur! What happiness! To slip and crash to the ground causing serious injury necessitating a long period of intensive institutional care! What could be more welcome? How your faith must be blossoming in the invigorating atmosphere of profound disability that surrounds you now! With what deep happiness I am sure you must survey those heavy weights depending from your helpless limbs, and look forward with a mighty leaping of your spirit to a further lengthy experience of enforced horizontality! On Saturday I shall be enabled to witness your good fortune personally when I am home for a weekend from college. I shall enter your ward with a dance of elation and greet you with a word of celebration.

Yours in joyful anticipation,

Charles Cook.

Dear Geruld,
          You gnow your friend
Charles at Deep Joy Bibul school
who sends me pecewliar letters?
Well the last one was all abowt
how fracchering your lemur and
being an attraction was acey-
pacey   brilliant and all.
Loony, eh?
          Ennyway, he came to see me
on saterday and he dansed into
the ward not loocking where he
was going and   stubbed his
big   toe on the end of a big
mettal thing and startid hopp-
ping around saying bad words
threw his teeth. It was grate!
I decided to cheer him up
Geruld, so I said — Oh to stub
a toe!   What happinness! What
ridundant joy to have a acey-pacey
pain in the foot! I wish I
was lucky old you hopping
abowt, Charles old chap! Let's
hope the luvvly agony larsts a

good long time, eh? Hallylooyah!

He was very cross for a littal while, Geruld, then he suddernly laughed, and he was nice like he ewesed to be and not like a robot. They must have speshul robot classes down at his school, eh? Do you have to get speshul permishun to be normal when yor a christiun, Geruld? If you don't, somewon ought to tell evvryone. I think so.

All my Logical Bonds

Andromeda.

Dear Andromeda,

I met Father John in the off-licence the other evening, and we were chatting about you. He said how much he'd enjoyed getting to know you, and how bravely he thought you were putting up with being stuck in that hospital bed and not having Mum and Dad around. One or two of the things he said made me think that you might be feeling a bit useless to God, and even worrying that you weren't good enough for him. When I talked to Anne about this she said I ought to send you the bit from my 'diary' when I had to give a talk on Spiritual Pride. She said, 'If God's still crazy about you despite things like that, then there's hope for anybody'. A bit of an exaggeration in my view, but it is true that I was rather thoughtless, and I'm sure you wouldn't have made the same mistakes. Father John says we're all members of the ratbag club, so we'd better stick together all we can, eh?

Anyway, here's my 'diary'. Your friend Leonard Thynn is in most of it . . .

Wednesday

Very flattered by Edwin asking me to speak on the subject of Spiritual Pride at next Sunday's service. Don't know why, but whenever I'm asked to do something like this, my spirituality seems to be cubed on the spot. Came away from the phone wanting to tell someone (in a humble sort of way) about Edwin's invitation. There was only Thynn there. He'd come round earlier for a meal without being invited *again*. I said, 'Edwin wants me to speak on Spiritual Pride next Sunday. I can't think why'.

'Because you're an expert on it I expect,' said Thynn, leaning back and taking the last pear from the fruit bowl.

Didn't bother to ask him what he meant. Why did God create things like locusts and earthquakes and Thynn?

I'm determined to do this talk really well. Must think of three headings beginning with the same letter . . .

Thursday

Thynn round tonight. Why doesn't he just move in and have done with it? Invited himself to go with Gerald to a meeting at some new local church. Asked which church it was. Gerald said it called itself the Holy and Apostolic True Church of the Abundant Revelation of Living Stones. Apparently it's a split from a break-away group which left the remnant of a disaffected portion of a dissenting faction from a fellowship that had separated itself from the original Holy and Apostolic True Church of the Abundant Revelation of Living Stones. According to Gerald, none of the present members realise that they've dissented themselves right back to the place where they started. I sometimes wonder if Gerald makes these things up . . .

Settled down after they'd gone out to plan my talk. Used a new concordance so that I can whizz from scriptural reference to scriptural reference like a real speaker. Managed to sort out two of my headings as 'Humility' and 'Holiness'. Bit stuck for a third, but it'll come!

Friday

Very difficult to work on my talk this evening. Thynn arrived at teatime and stayed until late. He and Gerald get very silly sometimes. Tonight they played Cluedo, sustituting the names of church members for the traditional ones. In the first game it turned out that Mrs Flushpool did it in the study with the candlestick; in the second one Richard Cook did it with a rope in the kitchen. Found all the cackling very off-putting. Eventually they noticed my tutting and asked what I was doing. Made the mistake of telling them I was searching for a third heading beginning with 'H'. I must be mad. They suggested Henry Cooper, Haggis, Horstead Keynes, Halitosis, Hippopotamus, Heat-rash, Ham rolls, and many, many more. Gerald doesn't seem to appreciate that this Spiritual Pride talk could be a foothold for me into the upper leadership of our church. Just to stop the flow of aitches I asked them how last night's meeting went.

Gerald said, 'You should've gone, Dad. It was good. Mostly for married people really.'

Thought how nice it was to see Gerald so serious for once. I said, 'What happened?'

Gerald said, 'Seven couples asked James Dobson into their lives.'

My son will end up as thunderbolt fodder, I swear he will . . .

Saturday

Still one blinking 'H' short! Unbelievably, Thynn was here *again*! Ignored all hints. He sat on the floor staring at our goldfish and singing The Green Green Grass of Home over and over again. Anne said there's probably something wrong that we don't know about, but what a pain! How can I work this thing out by tomorrow with Thynn doing Tom Jones impressions all over the carpet?

1.00 am. Still only got two headings beginning with 'H'. Too tired now. I'll get up early and work on it.

Sunday

Church.

Took my Cruden's Concordance to the meeting with me. Went through the aitches secretly during the prayers, still looking for my third heading. Only half realised that Leonard had gone up to the front to give a testimony. Sat up and took notice when I saw by my watch that he was running over the time when I was supposed to start my talk. Glared at him until I found myself listening to what he was saying.

'. . . and this last week – well, not exactly a week to be precise, more like eight days – it's been very, very thingy. Difficult, I mean, very, very difficult not to err . . . not to err . . . do it – drink, I mean. Not that it's wrong for anyone else to drink of course – well, it might be if they'd got the same problem as me – but not err . . . normally. Where was I? Oh, yes, very difficult over the last approximate err . . . week. So every time – nearly every time I felt like going out and err . . . abusing my – for want of a better word – body, I went to the Plasses'. Not to abuse my body I don't mean. Good heavens, no! No, I just know they'd never err . . . turn me away, as it were, and I could just stay there until the old oojermaflip – the old whatsitsname – the old temptation err . . . went away. Nothing like having people who treat you like one of the old thingy – family – know what I mean? Just want to say how, well . . . how much I – you know . . .'

Realised my third heading was 'Hopeless' – me, I mean. Told everyone that, when I got up to do my (short) talk. Invited Thynn home for lunch afterwards, and thanked him privately in the kitchen for trusting us. He went red and knocked a full bottle of milk onto the floor.

I asked Gerald later what he really thought of James Dobson.

He said, 'Dad, I would go so far as to say that he's a combination of two of the greatest names in the Old Testament.'

I said, 'What do you mean?'

'Ah,' said Gerald, 'you see, James Dobson is an anagram of "Moses and Job".'

Mmmmm . . .

I don't really think you've got much to worry about, Andromeda, do you?

Love to you and Lucky Lucy,

From Uncle Adrian.

Dear Madam,

I write to you once again on the subject of toasters in general, and one toaster in particular: namely the electrical appliance which I purchased at your emporium some two or three weeks ago. Now, I am a broad-minded, flexible man, but I have certain stubborn, possibly even prejudiced, views on the ideal function of such machines. My idea, and you may wish to dismiss it out of hand as being wild and fanciful, is that one should be able to place slices of bread into the appliance and, a minute or two later, remove them in a toasted state. An eccentric whim perhaps, but there is a surprisingly substantial body of opinion which freely endorses such a view, and I feel it may be of benefit to you to be aware of this new and revolutionary movement in case other customers in your establishment should purchase similar pieces of equipment and take them home with just such a narrow expectation lodged in their minds. Let me suggest one or two minor refinements that may be thought useful in the particular model with which you supplied me.

At one end of the machine is a small dial, which can be turned from a point marked 'LIGHT' to a point marked 'DARK'. It was in connection with this dial that I made my first error. The morning after my purchase I was obliged to rise at a very early hour before the sun rose and while the temperature was uncomfortably low. Happily, my home is very adequately lit and heated by electric power so I was able to reasonably anticipate a pleasant breakfast in warm surroundings before commencing the day's duties. Having placed two slices of bread into the 'toaster', I then turned the aforementioned dial to 'DARK', and pressed down the lever which, I assumed, would simply lower the bread into the inner recesses of the appliance. How I ever contracted the lunatic idea that 'LIGHT' and 'DARK' referred to the degree of toasting required, I really could not say. But, though I say it myself, I am a fast learner. As the lights went out and the entire electrical system in my house ceased to function, I realised how foolish I had been. Turning the dial to 'LIGHT', however, did not restore the general illumination.

Much later, and after considerable expenditure on the services of an electrician, my lighting and power were restored, and your machine had been cleverly converted into something approaching the appliance I had originally envisaged. I say 'something approaching' because there are still some very minor improvements that might be possible. May I suggest, for instance, that the terms 'LIGHT' and 'DARK' should be replaced on similar machines with the terms 'NOT TOASTED AT ALL' and 'CREMATED'. Alternatively, and I slip this in merely as a little personal preference, might it be possible to produce a radically new variety of appliance which toasts bread to the degree required by the appliance's owner?

I do hope that you will not feel I am fussing over trivial details, and I look forward with eager anticipation to continuing a dialogue on this subject when I bring your 'toaster' back to visit you later in the week. I should love to hear your views on refunding, or the exchange of faulty goods.

Yours sincerely,

Percival X Brain (Elderly and frail)

P.S. Looking back through my files, I note that I have already written to you twice on this matter. I hope you will not brand me a fanatic. Did you know, by the way, that there is an old tradition, still upheld in some parts of the country, of actually replying to letters?

Dear Geruld,

I have had a letter from your naybour, Mister Brain, ackewsing me of selling him a crabby old toester. I gnow being an attraction mite do funny things to the mined, but shorely I'd rememba if I'd sett up a bizness selling forlty ~~elec~~ elecrital stuff to old men. Eh? Shorely! Mister Brain mite have got a bit seenile in the head, beeing old and aul. It carn't be easy when yor name is Brain and most of it's gon.

Cood you arsk him to eggsplane pleese, Geruld?

Lucky Lucy says HALLO GERULD.

Logical bonds
Andy - pandy xx

P.S. I've put Mister Brain's loony letter in for you to Peru's. (good werd eh, Geruld. It meens look at).

147

Dear Andy Pandy,

What a scream! What a panic! What a to-do! Thank goodness you sent me that letter! Bless your little cotton socks, you prevented an innocent man from being dragged off to the cells. It was real drama – just like on the television. I'll tell you what happened. Ready? Okay!

I got your letter telling me about Mister Brain and the toaster after I came home from college the day before yesterday. (I came home at two o'clock in the afternoon, but don't tell Mother – she doesn't think college counts if you haven't been there *all* day). I went straight round after I'd read it to see old Percy and ask him what was going on. 'Toasters?' I thought. 'Funny!' I thought. Anyway, he wasn't there, so I thought I'd try again after tea. I was going to ask Dad what he thought about it, but I chickened out in the end. Dad's got a heart of gold, but – well, what's the point of complicating things? So, about seven o'clock, I stepped out of our front door to climb the fence to Percy's place. Then I stopped dead, because what do you think I saw standing outside Mister Brain's house?

Well, what do you think?

Come on – have a guess!

You can't? Right! I'll tell you then.

It was a police car, Andy Pandy, with an orange stripe all round it and a blue light on top, sitting there as large as life. For a moment I thought I'd better go back inside and mind my own business, but I just couldn't. I WAS NOSEY!!!! Awful, isn't it, Love and a Dream? God has to forgive me for something or other every single day. (Wish I was perfect like you.)

Anyway! Like I said, I was too nosey to leave it, so I hopped over the fence and up to Percy's back door, which I found wide open. In I walked, all innocent, and through in the front sitting-room I found a scene like something out of a bad play. There were two policemen in full uniform looking all stern and stiff, and standing between them was a lady who – well, she was one of those tall, angular ladies who look as if they've put their make-up on in the dark with a shaving brush. And she was looking *very* angry. All three of them were glaring at Percy Brain as if he was the lowest sort of criminal there was. Now, I don't know if you realise this, but Mister Brain used to be an actor, Andy Pandy, throwing his arms about with a loud voice on a big stage – that sort of thing. He looked just like that now, crouched back against the wall with one hand over his heart, and the other thrust out in front of him as if he was trying to keep vampires away. And his eyes! They were wide and crazy looking, and his mouth was hanging open. He was *really* laying it on thick, was old Percy, but he was a bit worried as well, I could tell. A bit pale and twitchy – know what I mean?

So then this lady held a piece of paper out in Percy's direction, and spoke like someone who's just been chewing on a slice of lemon.

'Do you deny,' she screeched, 'writing this letter threatening to cripple me with your car if I don't give you a new toaster?'

'Threatening? . . . cripple? . . . toaster?' gasped Percy. 'I totally, absolutely, categorically deny sending *any* such letter!'

Well, then she read out loud from this piece of paper, and this is how it went.

'Dear young lady,

What an unfortunate accident a broken leg is! The pain must be *very* unpleasant. It is amazing, is it not, how easily such things can occur when we least expect them. Goodness me, you could be immobile in hospital for many weeks with such an injury. Some claim that such occurrences are the consequences of less than virtuous treatment of others, but this is surely not the case. You, for instance, might step into the street and be hit by a car whose driver, for one reason or another, has failed to pay sufficient attention. I, myself, might easily make this kind of mistake. I could make it tomorrow! I intend to visit you *very* soon, so I will not write more now. I wonder if you remember me? I *do* hope so! Look out for me.

Yours in anticipation,

Percival X Brain.

Yes, you guessed it, Andy! Poor old Percy had got his letters mixed. The lady in the toaster shop got the one meant for you, and you got the one complaining about the toaster. Good job I was on the spot with the other letter, wasn't it? All sorted out in the end. The boys in blue were in stitches – they thought it was hilarious. I got a feeling the lady was a bit disappointed really, though. I think she'd hoped Percy would be taken out and hung from the nearest lamp post. Tried to explain it all to Dad later, but I might as well have tried to strike a match on jelly.

Love to Lucky Lucy and, of course, Andy Pandy,

Gerald.

PART V

10, Drowning Street,
  London,
  Youknighted Kingdum.

Dear Misses Thacher,
        Have you ever bean an attraction? I doon't think so. Not on the natural helth ennyway. I am pubblickly horizontall and prowd of it. I bet you woodn't have yor lemur mended by an uncwollified sturgeon called <u>Mister</u> Fisher. My name is Veal by the way. I leen to the left and I am a bit red. My muther is up with the green and common wimmen and Gwendd, still tryeing too get rid of the crude rissoles. I bleeve you are verry kean on Mister Raygun's base, Misses Thacher, like that man with a nayme that sownds lik a beddtime drink who had an affare with a hellicopter and climed out of the cabinet to sulk after you told him off. Well I'm <u>knot</u>! Why doon't you tell Mister

Raygun to keep his rissoles in his own base? How meny people have to becum green and common befor you see cents? Eh? If I can werk it out with grate weights hanging off my ancles, shorely you can do it vertikal! You havvnt got grate weights on you. Hou is yor son Mark? Father said that Mark Thacher is an ambishun, not a persun. It's the only thyme I ever saw farther and Gwenda agree. Farther spoilt it a bit later when Gwenda said — Arn't you intarested in batterd wimmen, and father said — yes, I'll have two large ones and a dubble porshun of chips pleese.

Annother thing Misses Thacher, can you do sumthing abowt Dugless Nurd's hare? Farther used to say he looks lyke an unhappee ice-creem cone in the wind. Why don't you get Weedwell Sosoon to give him a bit of a trimm? Father said if you stuck a sigar in his ear heed look lyke a 99.

Ennyway, aul I can say is wot abowt a ewe-turn Misses Thacher? If you beecame a soshulist lots of the uther stories mite get a bit less blue. Eh? Mister Kinnerk mite give you a job if you do. Grarnted you woodn't be abul to be Frying Mincer and hav yor own persunnel defective, but you wood at leest avoid beeing infiltraighted when the reverlooshun cums. I am in tuch with Mister Georgeous chops. I cood put in a werd for you.

yors in antissipayshun

Andromeda Veal (Mizz)

P.S. Witch one is yor persunnel defective? Is it the one with gray hare and glasses?

Telephone (Decided not to reconnect after scripture
revealed it was visiting 'friends' who
ran up the huge bill.
Jeremiah 12:6 'They have called a multitude.')

Dear Brother or Sister,

Please excuse the hand-written pink crayon on shiny
toilet paper, but when Stanley left the Project with my
other assistant, he took his John Bull printing set with him,
and I have run out of paper bags.

As you will note from the new project title, a revelation
has once again been vouchsafed to me, and we are, in
obedience, setting out on a new course. When I say 'we', I
mean in fact 'I'. Like Gideon of old I have seen the fearful
and the kneelers removed from my midst, and I alone am
continuing the work set before me. Stanley and Bruce are
singularly lacking in vision and adaptability. Stanley in
particular seeming to surrender to a spirit of moroseness
after his unfortunate experience at the Frog and Spittle on
amateur night. I reminded him that there are worse fates
than being covered with beer by a drunken audience intent
on making a fool of you because you tried to play the spoons
with only one spoon and no experience whatsoever, but he
appeared unconvinced. Bruce was infected by this negative
attitude to such an extent that when I announced the
termination of the musical project they were both unripe
for change, and decided to leave.

The new, and certainly most exciting project to date, will
involve the hauling of a thirty-five foot wooden Victorian

church pew through every country in the entire world, on foot. Preparations are complete, other than details such as finding a suitable pew, talking its owner into giving or selling it to me, working out how to move it, planning a route, sorting out passport and visas, amassing sufficient finance for the journey and selling the prefab. Once again I am absolutely determined that this will be a faith venture, and already I have received a firm offer of the loan of a screwdriver as and when I locate a suitable pew. I regard this as strong confirmation of guidance received thus far.

Over the last week or two I have been touring the local churches speaking to groups about my unwillingness to publicise the project purely for the purpose of raising much needed capital. I always take with me a pile of the sort of financial pledge form that I do *not* want filled in by those who are seeking only to salve their consciences. I enclose such a form with this letter. Please strike out either 'I give willingly to the Lord', or 'I intend to keep my money for my own selfish pleasures and I don't see why God should get his hands on it', then sign the form and return it to me. Please do *not* feel pressured to respond in a particular way.

Yours,

Vernon Rawlings (sic sec)

P.S. A fresh revelation this morning. Clear indication from scripture that I should sail my pew like a raft around the oceans. Ezekiel 28:2 'I am sitting on the seat of God, surrounded by the seas'.

P.P.S. Please pray for a paddle.

Dear Rabbit Runcie,

I am a non-anglian attraction cauled Mizz A. Veal. The onley uther one of yors I gnow is the Neverend Boom who has a bit of trubble soughting out what's a dimmonimation and what's a brekkfust serial. Rest ashored I have aulso written to the Pope abowt mayking babys do the limbo and that, so I'm not just gettting at yew Rabbit old chapp. My frend Geruld (his persunnel problum is the onley thing that's maid beeing horizontall beardabull) says yor name is a nammagranamm of C. E. but inerror, so he mus lyke you two. Eh? One thing yor lukky abowt is yew doon't have to be a halibut like my frend Farther John at the nunkery or the Pope in his Fattycan, but I have a fealing yor not quyte asin charje as the Pope. He can say wot he lykes withowt feer of contraception from the catlicks eeven if the cardiggans get stroppy, but yew have to mayke speechis at a speshul plaice cauled the Sinodd. My frend Geruld says it's maid up of sum peeple who've been ordrained, lyke beacons and curits and shotguns and bish ups and rectums, and the rest are drorn from the ~~the~~ Layertee (whoevver they mite be when there at home, eh Rabbit?), but they aul have to be peeple who lyke to Sinodd, and evvrywon torks and torks for ajes and ajes and then decides to leeve evvrything lyke it wos befor. Sounds a bit of a waist of thyme to me, Rabbit, but I eggspect you gnow best beeing the arch bish up.

Ooh, Rabbit! I wish I'd been yew marreeing Prints Charls and Laidy Die! I saw it on a film. I gnow they are bluddsukkers on the tyred flesh of the British proldairyfat, but I think their aceypacey skill and aul. I lyke the ~~queen~~ queen two, eeven tho I'm not aloud to rearly. Shee nearly cryed when thay got married by yew, diddn't she? Wozzn't it nice of the inshorance cumpany to lend you their bilding for the day? I hope you wrote them a thancyou letta. Did you Rabbit? It's only plite.

Rabbit, wot is a bish up? It sownds lyke a missteak of sum kind, but why do yew keep mayking new ones if that's wot they are? Wot woz aul that fuss abowt the Durrem one who said things abowt the verging berth and the west direction of Jesus? He is a bish up, isn't he? He is cauled the bish up of Durrem, lyke the Grate fyre of London, eh? I think he looks nyce, but praps he shood have stuck to sprinting.

Ennyway, wot I wonted to arsk woz, sumtimes when yor going up and down the Lambuth Warlk, cood yew just remined God that Andromeda is waiting with a unknit lemur for a bitt of actiun green and common wimmen - wise?

Good on yer, Rabbit! Lucky Lucy says thancyou two. She is my first dolly sins Bigot, and I am keaping her eeven if I lern the wrong roll in serciety.

Logical Bonds to you
and aul the bish ups,

Andromeda Veal (Mizz)

P.S. My frend Geruld says his nice fashist dad's car must beelong to the Cherch of England becos it onley goes in for a service twyce a year. Goodun', eh?

P.P.S. If yew and the Pope beleeve in the same God wot's so speshul abowt cantering through Walkerbury Catheedrul togetha? Eh? For goodniss sake!

Dear Andromeda,

Gerald says you very much enjoyed the last extract from my diary that you saw – the bit about my talk on Spiritual Pride – and that you wouldn't mind seeing some more. I'm *very* pleased that you enjoy my diary so much. I sometimes think that Gerald, and even Auntie Anne sometimes, don't really understand that you can learn things from experiences recorded in this way. I have known Gerald to sit with tears of laughter running down his face whilst reading an entry that doesn't appear even remotely humorous to *me*. Still, he's a good, kind lad, so I don't really mind.

By the way, I'm really pleased you liked your doll. We went right through two shops before we found one that looked right. We had to leave the first shop we tried because the manageress foolishly took offence at some perfectly innocent remarks I happened to be making to unsuitable

163

dollies, but in the end we met Lucy and all agreed that she was the one. We *did* enjoy leaving her on the pillow beside you. Dear Andromeda – I felt so sorry for you stuck in that bed for so long. I'm glad you think I'm a *good* fashist now. I hope I'm good. I do try, but I seem to get in such a tangle sometimes. When I wanted someone to do the chairs at church for instance. It was really . . . well, that's the bit of the diary I've put in for you to look at. Hope you find it interesting.

Monday

Edwin, our Elder, rang to ask if the study group I lead could take responsibility for putting out the chairs at church every Saturday evening ready for Sunday. I said, 'No problem, Edwin!'. Felt rather proud of my 'team'.

Phoned Stenneth Flushpool and asked if he'd do it. He said he'd commit it to the Lord in prayer, and ask his wife. Gerald was listening. Said that if God and Mrs Flushpool disagreed he wouldn't put much money on God's chances.

Tried Richard Cook next. He said that it was unscriptural to make definite plans for the future, so he couldn't promise to do it every week, but 'as the Lord leadeth'. Asked him how far in advance he reckoned the Lord might let him know each time. He said, 'It is not for us to know, but may your faith be equal to the test, Brother'.

I have discovered that you can't strangle telephones . . .

Tuesday

Vernon Rawlings (one of my study group) gave a talk tonight at the monthly church meeting about sacrificial giving. Very strong and inspiring. So impressive I started making notes near the beginning. Last bit went as follows:

'. . . and let's face it, brothers and sisters, when we talk about giving we usually mean parting with a small part of our surplus. We pay lip service to the Christian ideals of love and charity, but when it really comes to the crunch, are we ready to give freely and cheerfully beyond the point of comfort? Are we, brothers and sisters? I want to ask you all . . .'

Vernon pointed dramatically at various members of the church as he went on in a loud voice.

'. . . young Christian boy! Young Christian girl! Brothers and sisters of middle age! Elderly friends! I want to challenge you right now! Are you prepared to give until it hurts? Are you prepared to take what you have in terms of money and possessions and time, and give whatever is needed to whoever needs it, or are you just going to play at religion by keeping the best for yourself and throwing a few scraps to your neighbour? I challenge you tonight, brothers and sisters! The next time someone comes up to you and asks you to give or do something, will you deny your faith and say 'NO!', or will you count the cost and, despite personal expense, say 'YES! I'll do it!' "

Collared Vernon straight afterwards and asked if he'd do the chairs. He said, 'No, I'd rather not. There's good telly on Saturday.'

Wednesday

Stenneth Flushpool rang. Said he had no inner peace about the chairs, and he wouldn't be allowed to do it anyway.

Richard Cook rang. Said he now felt that the Lord would have him stand with me in prayer about the chairs, and would that do?

Tried Percy Brain. He said that when I'd tried everyone in the entire universe and still wasn't able to get anyone, then he *might*, *possibly* help *very* occasionally, but that would depend on circumstances at the time, so it was better

165

to rule him out other than *very, very* exceptionally. And even then he couldn't promise.

Thanked him for sparing the time to talk to me . . .

Sat down by the telephone and rang *all* the others. Never heard such a load of feeble, pathetic excuses in all my life. Bit fed up with my 'team' by the time I finished. What a list!

William Farmer: Bad leg, which for some lunatic reason means he can't use his arms.

Leonard Thynn: Chairophobia (?)

Norma Twill: Didn't want to spoil the sensitive soft skin on her hands.

Ephraim Trench: Said he'd disagreed with buying this particular set of chairs thirty-seven years ago, and his integrity would be in question if he was seen to be helping with them now.

Raymond Pond: Said his ministry was in music, not chair arranging, and could I ask whoever *did* do it to stay well away from the organ please?

Honestly!

Thursday

Study group tonight. At the end I really stormed at everyone about the chairs. Pointed out that *no one* had offered to help.

'And because of that,' I concluded, 'we all know who's going to end up doing the chairs every Saturday evening – Anne!'

After they'd all gone off looking very subdued, Anne said, 'Darling, I didn't want to say anything in front of everybody, but I don't quite understand why I'm the obvious choice to do the chairs.'

'What do you mean?' I said, a little shocked.

Anne said, 'Well, why shouldn't you do it, for instance?'

'Don't be silly,' I said, 'you know Saturday's the night when I always like to – ah, I see what you mean . . .'

166

Friday

Good job I'm a Christian. If I wasn't I'd tot up all the things I've done for my study group members and send each one a bill. As it is I naturally forgive them freely for being so selfish.

Saturday

Gerald offered to come down with me to help with the chairs this evening. Surprised to find the front door left unlocked. Even more surprised to find nearly all of my study group inside! They'd turned up to help with the chairs! Organised a rota for the future and got on with it.

Norma wore gloves.

Ephraim supervised.

Thynn kept his eyes shut.

William hopped.

Gerald spent the entire time working out that Alex Buchanan is an anagram of 'Ex-banana hulc'.

Went home feeling quite warmed inside.

So you see, Andromeda, it all got sorted out in the end. It usually does. It's the sorting out bit that seems to get complicated. When I get to heaven I've got a few questions to ask God . . .

Love to Lucky Lucy and you,

Uncle Adrian.

P.S. Why don't you work out an anagram for Gerald's name? I did once. I think he was quite impressed. By the way, your Uncle Edwin's planning to come and see you tomorrow.

Dear Andromeda,

After visiting you last night I've decided to write to you because I'm afraid you might be getting a little confused. Mind you, I don't blame you! With everything that's happened to you and your family I would be surprised if you hadn't got things a *bit* upside-down.

As you know, Andromeda, I'm the Elder at my church and I think most of the people who go there think I'm not too bad at the job, but nearly all of them reckon I've one main fault. I wonder if you can guess what it is. You're *very* good at saying exactly what you think, so you might find it rather hard to understand! My problem is that I hardly *ever* speak out loud and clear about what I think and believe. People think I should do it much more often (especially when they think someone else has gone wrong!), but I just carry on in my own way most of the time – people who've got problems or aren't quite sure about things seem to find it easier to get close if I don't make too much noise. After talking to you last night though, I thought I ought to be more 'LOUD AND CLEAR' than usual. You see, I know how angry and upset you must be about your mother and father going off and leaving you at a time when you need them so much, and I'm sure I'd feel exactly the same. I just want to say one or two things to you. First, there's nothing wrong with what your Mum's doing. She believes very strongly in what's happening among the protestors up at the missile bases and we need people in this country who are willing to do more than just *talk* about things being wrong. I admire your Mother very much, and I think very highly of your Dad too. He just got fed up with not feeling very important, and started saying unkind things and making the kind of jokes that he *knew* would upset your Mum and Gwenda until things got so bad that he had to leave. Now, I know it sounds as if I'm just having a go at your parents, but it's only because I can remember just the same thing happening to me. You see, when your Auntie Joan and I moved down here and I took over the eldership of a church for the first time, I made the same sort of mistakes that I think your Mum might be making. I was quite young and very anxious that everything should go really well in the church, and it never occurred to me that Auntie Joan and our two little girls needed me at home just as much or more than most of the people in the church. I was out just about *every* evening, Andromeda, doing what I thought of as 'The Lord's Work', and if I'm really honest, I quite often made sure that 'The Lord's Work' started just before the time when the girls had to be bathed and put in bed and read to. I was never there, Andromeda! And if anyone had said to me, 'Do you love your family?', I'd have got very stiff and indignant and said, 'What *do* you mean? Of course I love them – I'm a church Elder!' I didn't understand you see. I came to my senses in the end when someone wise and kind gave me a bit of a telling off, but it went on for quite a long time, with poor Auntie Joan just having to put up with it because every time she complained I said that I was only doing what God told me to do. The things I was doing were good and useful and all that – it's just that I didn't realise (or didn't let myself realise) that there were even more important things to be done in my very own home. Maybe that's what's been happening with your Mum, Andromeda. There's no doubt she loves you, and your Dad's potty about you – always has been. I think they just let things go too far and get too bad, and in the end neither of them could stand it, so away they went, leaving you in the middle, sweetheart. It happens to an awful lot of children I'm afraid. But don't give up. I haven't. Your Mum and Dad were always great pals underneath everything and my guess is that they probably still are. Keep badgering God, and so will I.

Your loving Uncle Edwin.

Dear Andromeda,

Victoria (Mrs Flushpool) has asked me – well, told me – I should write you a letter. My name is Stenneth Flushpool and I am married to Mrs Flushpool (Victoria). You may be a little puzzled by my name. I am called Stenneth as the result of a disagreement between my parents. At my christening the vicar asked in which name I was to be baptised, and my father replied, 'Kenneth'. Simultaneously, my mother, a rather dominant lady, not unlike Victoria (Mrs Flushpool), replied 'Stanley'. The Vicar, an elderly man with somewhat impaired hearing, interpreted this confusion of sounds as the word 'Stenneth', and baptised me accordingly. My parents decided to accept this accidental compromise in the interests of peace, and I have been Stenneth ever since. I cannot say it has been a happy accident for me. There is invariably a short pause when I am introduced to a new acquaintance, while the person concerned controls his or her features and deals with the rising gust of mirth which the mention of my name always seems to precipitate. Do you find my name amusing?

However, enough of that. Victoria (Mrs Flushpool) was of the opinion that the bulk of my letter to you should consist of relevant and instructional verses from scripture, together with helpful anecdotes of testimony from my own life. I am not, however, bound to abide by the wishes of Mrs Flushpool (Victoria). It has been suggested that I am unduly influenced and even dictated to by Victoria (Mrs Flushpool), but this is not wholly the case. Last week, for instance, I was adamant that I would select my own new pinny for work in the kitchen. It is essential to win these battles from time to time. But I digress. The fact is, Andromeda, that I was myself obliged to remain in hospital for a long period in traction some four years ago. In my case it was a back problem, but I did experience all the same physical discomforts and indignities that you are undergoing now, and I would like you to know that you have my deepest sympathy. I would also, if you do not mind, like to share a confidence with you that I have shared with no other person, and particularly not with Mrs Flushpool (Victoria). You see, despite all the discomfort, I really rather *enjoyed* my stay in hospital. It was not unlike an extended holiday. Many of the nurses who cared for me were pretty, friendly girls, and I experienced a most unusual sense of specialness whilst lying so helplessly in my bed. Naturally I was *deeply* conscious of the absence of Victoria (Mrs Flushpool), but she did visit every other day to read lengthy extracts from holy literature for the whole of the visiting period. I find it difficult to express my appreciation of such devotion. On those occasions when she was not present though, I indulged myself in two areas, of which, I fear, Mrs Flushpool (Victoria) would not have approved. First, I managed to persuade one of the porters (a Mr Blogg if I remember rightly) to bring me some magazines on model aircraft construction, an activity which Victoria (Mrs Flushpool) regards (I believe mistakenly, though I say nothing) with some suspicion. These afforded me immense satisfaction, but it was my other activity that occupied most of my unvisited time. (Why I should be writing all this to a young person like yourself, I really could not say.) My other activity arose out of my dissatisfaction with my name – Stenneth. I spent very considerable periods simply imagining that my name was Kirk C. Flushpool (the C stood for Craig). Most of these imaginings were in the form of dialogue between myself and a new acquaintance. Here are some examples:

New Acq : Hello, you're a fine looking chap. What's your name?
Me   : Kirk, actually.
New A   : What a great name! What's your middle name?

171

Me	:	Craig.
New A	:	My name's only Paul. I wish I was called Kirk Craig!
Me	:	They're only names. Paul's nice.

This is one I used to pretend was a telephone conversation from work.

Me	:	Hi! Flushpool here, K.C. Flushpool. Do you want to buy some of our goods?
Customer	:	That name sounds terrific! What does the K.C. stand for?
Me	:	Only Kirk Craig. Very ordinary names really.
Customer	:	Ordinary names my foot! They're great names, and I bet you live up to them.
Me	:	Oh, I don't know.
Customer	:	Well, look, Kirk . . .
Me	:	Yes?
Customer	:	I'd like to put in a really big order, as long as it's you who handles it. Okay, Kirk?
Me	:	Sure thing! Kirk out.

This must appear very foolish to you, Andromeda, but I enjoyed these little pretendings very much indeed, and I still think about those weeks in the ward sometimes, although I do not mention such things to Mrs Flushpool (Victoria). I fear she would not understand.

Do forgive me for writing a letter that seems, now that I look back at it, mostly about me, but I have greatly appreciated the opportunity to express myself a little on paper. I do hope you are soon well enough to return home.

Yours sincerely,

Stenneth Flushpool.

P.S. Please bear in mind when/if replying that Victoria (Mrs Flushpool) is not aware of the contents of this letter. I do not intend deceit, but unnecessary upset would be rather unfortunate.

P.P.S. Please do not think that I am not sympathetic with Mrs Flushpool (Victoria). I think that if we had been able to have the child that we both so much wanted, she would have been a lot less – stern.

Dear Mister Flushpool, (It wood be districtspeckful of me two caul you Stennith).

Thankyou for yor Letta. The scrippcher versis and anicdotes were rearly grate! Acey-pacey eggsiting and good four me and aul. (Nudje, nudje, wink-wink, eh?) Pleese give my rigards to Misses Flushpool (Euston), and say that I wood be pleesed to see her ennytime, eeven if I'm asleep. In fact if shee's thinking of cumming to kindely read me lencthy eggstracts from holey lichrercher, it wood be betta if I was asleep becos sientists say you can lern a lot in yor brain wile yor asleep. Eh? I think so.

By the way, I arsked Mr. Blogg if he remembered you when you were in here. He said — O yes, that bloke wot wanted magazeens about scripcher and that brort in, he wos orlright he wos - so he does rememba you Mister Flushpool. (I cept my fingas crossed while I wrote the bit abowt the maga-

zeens, Mister Flushpool) Mr. Blogg
can burp wenever he wants to by
the way. I wish I cood burp wenever I wanted to. Pleese inquire
of yor wife whether she can burp
wenever she wonts to. Tell her yew
have to be carefull it cums out
the rite end.

Ennyway, that's dul for now from
yor frendly littal horizontall
attraction.
                    Logical Bonds
                        Andromeda

P.S. I doon't think Stennith is a
funnee name (just in case you wundered
wether I thort it was) I think it's a
sweet nayme. I think yor rather sweet,
Mister Flushpool, axshully.

P.P.S. If yew shood happen to meat an
old frend of mine cauled Kirk Craig
Something-or-other, cood you tell
him how mutch I like his names?

P.P.P.S. Perhapps Misses Flushpool
(Paddington) will have a lot less

175

stern as thyme goes by. It wos
sad wot you wrote larst. Nevver
to have a George. Eh?

Dear Geruld,

Gess what! If I spell yor name aul wrong with a A instead of a U, yor a nammagranam of —

SLADE SPRALG!

Goodun, eh? It makes you sownd like a acey-pacey weerdo film star.

By the way, Geruld. I thort I'd just menshun that it's my berthday next friday. I'm not remineding you in case youd forgottun you were going to give mee a brand new persunnel problem aul of my own, Geruld. I'm just men-shuning it in passing. I doon't mined if you forgett to give me one

Logical bonds (to Sladey-baby)

Andy-Pandy X

P. S.   It's this friday cumming when I doon't mined you forgetting to give me a brand new persunnel problem aul of my own, Geruld. The one just cumming up at the end of this week.

P. P. S. Thanckyou for lending me your persunnel problem aul this time (like what I havvn't got one of my own of).

Dear Andy Pandy,

Hi! It's Slade Spralg here. How's tricks? Now listen carefully my little love and a dream – or read carefully rather – because I'm putting my life in your hands. If Dad finds out I've sent you this bit of his diary there's likely to be another attraction down your way soon. One called Gerald. You see, Dad doesn't come over all that dignified in this extract from his great classical work. Mind you, he doesn't come over all that dignified in *any* of his entries, but this one is – well, you read it and see. And if you see Dad coming – eat it!

Monday

Why did God let cars be invented? Nothing but trouble and expense! In all the Christian paperbacks people travel fifty miles with no engine and four flat tyres almost every other day, just by the power of prayer. My cars have all been unbelievers. They sigh and give up. Even when *I* think they're okay someone else thinks they're not. Like this morning. Took my perfectly good car up to Ernie Pavement, our Christian mechanic, for its MOT. None of us has ever seen Ernie laugh. When Gerald told him we wanted a fully charismatic gearbox fitted in our last car, he said he didn't stock them. That's what made this morning so upsetting. He started by walking slowly round, staring sadly at it like someone watching a close relative die. Then, before I could tell him what I wanted, he patted me gently on the shoulder and suggested in a low, mournful voice that I should just walk quietly away without looking back and he'd see to its disposal.

I said, 'No Ernie, it's a perfectly good car! I don't want it disposed of. I want you to put it through its MOT.'

That's when he started this dreadful grating, helpless laughter. Ended up hanging over the bonnet wiping tears from his eyes with an oily rag. Good job for his sake the grease gun wasn't a couple of feet nearer my hand.

Gritted my teeth. 'Well, at least LOOK at it!' I said.

He walked round it again, poking bits here and there, and making clucking noises with his tongue, then he said, 'Looks like a resurrection job, mate.'

Asked him what he meant.

He said, 'Needs a completely new body.'

Went home very depressed (although inwardly rejoicing on some deep level of course). Wondered how I'd ever be able to afford a new car. Prayed about it, and suddenly in my mind's eye saw a brand new Volvo Estate!

Claimed it.

Tuesday

Saw fleets of new Volvos in my dreams all night. Told

Anne over breakfast that I felt we were being led into praying for a brand new Volvo Estate, but she displayed what to my mind is lamentable faithlessness.

She said, 'Let's be realistic, darling. We're looking at something small, economical, probably second or third hand and easy to park.'

Gerald stopped overeating for a moment to offer to sell us his old skateboard if we wanted it. Stupid boy!

Told Anne that I was going to believe for a new Volvo Estate. She said she thought it was much more likely to be something like a ten year old Datsun. We agreed that we'd each look for confirmation between now and Saturday.

Wednesday

Extraordinary! Everywhere I go the roads seem to be packed with Volvos. Counted twenty-three. A real sign!

When Anne came home she said she'd seen *twenty-four* Datsuns. Bit of a blow really . . .

Thursday

Counted eighteen Volvos today. Anne's score was thirteen Datsuns. I'm winning by four Volvos on aggregate! I don't like to doubt Anne, but I find her claim that she's hardly noticed any Volvos on the road very hard to accept. On the contrary. I don't understand where all these Datsuns appear from. I can't recall seeing *any*.

Friday

Excellent Volvo crop today. Anne went one better with her ridiculous Datsuns, but I'm still winning overall.

Leonard Thynn round tonight. You can always tell when Thynn thinks he's got something funny to say. He tries to look cool. Told me part of my car problem is solved because he's found a scripture verse in which God promises to arrange transport home from work for believers. Asked wearily which one it was.

He said, 'Isaiah, chapter twenty-two, verse nineteen. "I will drive you from your office".'

Thynn and Gerald cackled away like parrots. Left them cackling. Thynn borrowed the cat without asking while I was upstairs. Asked Anne tonight what he does with our cat. She looked surprised and said, 'That's just what I was going to ask you, darling. I thought *you* knew.'

One of these days I shall follow him . . .

Saturday

Saw THIRTY-FOUR Volvos today! Absolute famine of Datsuns. Hurried home to announce final confirmation of my leading. Anne arrived just after me. Said she'd seen seven hundred and sixty-three Datsuns! Turns out Gerald took her over to the Datsun factory by bus. Gerald said, 'Is that guidance, or is that guidance, Dad?'

Was just about to accuse them of cheating when Ernie Pavement arrived at the door. Said sadly that he'd found a car for us. Escort. Five years old. Good nick. Only one problem – the heater didn't work. Quite cheap. Did we want it?

Went for a drive in our new car later with Gerald. Saw no end of Volvos *and* Datsuns. Curious!

Car went well. Terribly cold though. I felt like a lump of frozen meat. Must get the heater fixed. Gerald pointed out that Old Escort is an anagram of Coldstore.

Feel a bit embarrassed about all that Volvo counting. Hope God wasn't watching – well, of course he *must* have been watching, but I hope – well . . .

What Dad doesn't realise, Andy Pandy, is that there never was a trip to any Datsun factory, and Mum never really kept a tally of Datsuns she saw on the roads. She was just kidding Dad along till he came out of his latest loony phase. Dear old Dad! He's a rather sweet old fashist, don't you think, Andy Pandy?

By the way, I happen to know why old Leonard borrows the cat. It's very ingenious really. You see, he turns on his reel to reel tape recorder, and then – well, I'll tell you about it when I visit next. It's not the sort of thing you can describe properly in a letter.

Give my love to Lucky Lucy and Rosy Roundway. See you soon.

Love, Gerald.

P.S. I'm just off to the shops to buy something for a friend's birthday.

P.P.S. Eh?

Dear Andromeda,

Exciting news! Your Mum rang last night to say that she's travelling down late on Thursday evening to be here for your birthday on Friday. She tried to ring the hospital but kept not getting through to the ward, so she rang us instead and asked if I would pass the message on. Oh, darling, I'm *so* pleased Mummy will be with you on your special day. She'll be on her own by the way. Gwenda's got engaged to a man who writes comedy for Channel 4, so she won't be protesting for a while. I've never heard your Mum sound so excited. She's really dying to see you, sweetheart.

By the way, Gerald will be popping in just for a few minutes on Friday to bring you – well, wait and see! Uncle Adrian and I will come over with our presents on Saturday if that's OK, so you'll have two birthdays really, won't you? And when you come out of hospital at last, you poor old thing, I think we ought to have a really nice late birthday party for you. What do you think?

We're still praying for you, Andromeda.

See you on Saturday.

Love, Auntie Anne X

Dear Andybugs,

I didn't *know* you were in hospital. Edwin contacted me last night. I honestly didn't know that you'd come a cropper and got laid up for so long. Everything went out of my head when I left home and I've just been working without stopping since then in a sort of daze. Andybugs, you do know that your silly old Dad loves you, don't you? Just because I went away doesn't mean I don't care, sweetheart. The other day at work someone asked me if I'd got any children, and I was about to be all grumpy and say mind your own business, when I suddenly saw you in my mind and felt really proud. 'Yes,' I said, 'I jolly well have got a child. She's the finest little girl in the whole world, and she's called Andromeda.' You *are* the finest little girl in the world, sweetheart, and Mother and I have done the rottenest job in the world looking after you. But maybe it's not too late to try. I don't know.

Listen, Andybugs. I can't get to you for a couple of days, but I'm on my way. I shall see you on Friday. OK? Save a big kiss and a hug for me. I'll be coming through that door to see you very soon, and I'm not going to go so far away ever again. Keep your chin up!

Love and kisses,

Daddy X X X

P.S. I haven't forgotten what day Friday is, love!

Dear God,

Don't do enny big relevash-
uns or angel cwires or that
because I'm writing this in the
middul of the night with a
torch (not eesy when yor horizontall, God). or Nurse
Roundway will tell us both off.
Being God won't help yew if
yew annoy Nurse Roundway, God!
Shee's a wholly terrer when
she's rowsed. That's why I'm
writing this in a whissper.
The rest of the ward's aul
quiet, but I'm too eggsited to
sleep. Gess what, God? I gnow
you gnow ennyway, but I want
to tell yew what's going to
happen on friday. Farther wrote
me a letter, God! He did! He
did! He wrote me a letter and
caulled me Andybugs and said
he'd come on friday and oh,
God, issn't it eggsiting! And
it's dubbly acey-pacey brill

eggsiting because mother's cumming on friday too! Oh, God, I'm a bit fritened about them seeing eech other. Oooh, I go aul tingly when I think abowt it! Enny chance of yew beeing here to reff the match, God? It is my birthday on friday, you know. Eh?

Ennyway, I'm going to try to go to sleep now. Do you sleep or are you bizzy sorting out Ostralia all night.

I'm glad I got to gnow yew.

Goodnight, God

Logical bonds,

Andromeda Veal (Mizz).